COACH FITZ

TOM LEE

Coach Fitz

GIRAMONDO

FIRST PUBLISHED 2018
FROM THE WRITING AND SOCIETY RESEARCH CENTRE
AT WESTERN SYDNEY UNIVERSITY
BY THE GIRAMONDO PUBLISHING COMPANY
PO BOX 752
ARTARMON NSW 1570 AUSTRALIA
WWW.GIRAMONDOPUBLISHING.COM

DESIGNED BY HARRY WILLIAMSON
TYPESET BY ANDREW DAVIES
IN 11/17 PT ADOBE GARAMOND PRO

PRINTED AND BOUND BY LIGARE BOOK PRINTERS
DISTRIBUTED IN AUSTRALIA BY NEWSOUTH BOOKS

A CATALOGUE RECORD FOR THIS
BOOK IS AVAILABLE FROM THE
NATIONAL LIBRARY OF AUSTRALIA.

ISBN: 978-1-925336-90-0

9 8 7 6 5 4 3 2 1

COACH FITZ

The naked human seeks out their trainer. Some find this person in their family. Some in friends. Others never find them. Others don't believe they need to.

I began with a small body. Late to mature, I measured myself against my thicker, hairier peers. I sought advice from the magazines that displayed the bodies I desired. I needed muscle, a good layer of it, to make up for my lack of pubic hair. My maturity was beyond my control, but to some extent the form of my body could be manipulated. I found an old bench and rusted weights out the back of the pottery shed at school.

With the routines from magazines memorised, and backdropped by spiderweb-ridden sclerophyll, I set to work on myself, twenty minutes an afternoon, two afternoons a week. Tuesdays, Thursdays. Wavering under the weight of steel: one, two, three, four. The smell of rusted metal mixed with sweat was evidence of my improvement.

I debuted my updated body some six months later in the school gym, with its forgiving wooden boards and black rubber mats, louvres, dust and radio. Benches in all variety of angles, some forcing the body into a beggar's posture, others like a breaking wheel, cages of steel, winches and pulleys isolated from any purpose other than to isolate muscle and put it under duress.

My routine grew more elaborate and my muscles more bulky. Half-known gym regulars clustered in surprise, my buddies came to watch, and soon, in the mirrors, thick seams of muscle emerged where before there'd been only bone.

We'd smoke cigarettes in the bush after working out. A congregation of fringe dwellers supposedly improving their prospects, manipulating blood flow one minute, sending smoke inwards the next, bound by a shared perversity in motive. The bush always there to look on as we began these first experiments in bodily stimulation.

Meeting One: Centennial Park

I received a notification that Coach Fitz had accepted my proposal. Since the death of my maternal grandfather, Peter, I had felt the presence of an emotional rift that I had the good sense to know might be trained into an advantage. I wrote as much to Coach Fitz in my proposal and she found this attitude promising. I also sent her some previous results that proved I was interested in using exercise to bring focus to my life. I had run some fairly solid times in the Sydney City2Surf in recent years, after promising and failing to compete in the race for many years prior.

On one such occasion my grandfather phoned me on the day of the race, presumably to ask how I had fared. I'd favoured a bottle of red wine and some lengthy discussion the night before and was going through a patch where my energies were messily directed. I let his phone call ring out. The pang of guilt arrived only later, but gradually a conviction crystallised: it was my duty to answer that call through a sustained program of athletic practice on the border between the amateur and the elite.

Coach Fitz was known for her unusual methods. I heard about her via a friend of a friend that had trained under her guidance while living in Melbourne in 2005. Rumour had it that she was an exceptional long-distance runner in her youth who then practised psychoanalysis in the UK before returning to Australia to combine her love of running with her understanding of the human mind. I found her contact details on the internet and flagged my interest in her program.

I include the details of my initial communication below.

My name is Tom. I grew up in central-west New South Wales and have always had a strong affection for running as a means of obtaining a sense of agency over a vast environment and maximising different perspectives on a place. I've run a sub-60 in the City2Surf. I surprised myself, especially considering I tend to drink alcohol and smoke cigarettes on weekends and at night. I usually run about three times a week. I mix it up with hills, soft sands, stairs, track running and longer runs. More than anything I just love being out and about covering as much ground as possible in beautiful Sydney. I seem to be drawn towards the coast or bushland for many of my running sessions, most of which are completed in the inner west and the eastern suburbs, and often involve a swim in the ocean afterwards. There is no better feeling than finishing a taxing run at Bronte and going for a dip.

I seem to have hit a bit of a plateau and really want to shave a few minutes off my time. Would you be able to offer a program that might suit my needs?

All the best,
Tom

In the troublingly swift reply that I would come to know as typical of her communications, Coach Fitz suggested we meet around dusk at the Robinson Gates in Centennial Park, where we could go for a relaxing long jog, get to know each other and discuss the form our partnership might take.

I parked my car on Robertson Road and made my way along the park fence down to the entrance. I had done an image search online to get an idea of what Coach Fitz looked like but it produced an array of unlikely candidates: a smiling man in a yellow construction worker's helmet appeared frequently, as well as a roughly hewn square of quiche.

I waited at the gate entrance, admiring the different vectors on show: people on horseback, scooters, bikes, rollerbladers, women with prams, joggers of all ages and shapes, cars reduced to a crawl and, most delightfully, a couple walking in a kind of train formation, one behind the other, bonded by two poles or ropes that each held in their hands and which responded to and accentuated the rhythm of their strides. The squawk of the lorikeets was deafening.

In the distance, about seventy or so metres off, I saw a figure running towards me. She was about five foot nine or ten, with short, very slightly bowed legs, a strikingly long torso and a compact, relaxed running style. I bent down to do up a lace and when I next stood the figure was almost upon me. She wore a floppy yellow legionnaire's cap, dark-blue lightweight shorts covered in pilling and a yellow t-shirt also heavily pilled. Tom, she extended a hand, top spot, scanning the surrounds with approval. Her unevenly cut, red-tinged hair was flecked with globules of unrubbed-in sunscreen, particularly around the ears, and bits of leaf matter and sand clinging to her forehead.

I replied in agreement and began with the usual pleasantries, about how much I'd heard about her and how excited I was. Coach pointed to four palm trees planted in a square on the grass slope before a quaint brick building with a veranda, which she would later identify as the Rangers Cottage. This is our temple, she said, it is here we will prepare our bodies.

We jogged lightly to the area between the trees and I immediately experienced the sense of occasion evoked by its strict geometric configuration. Coach balanced herself against one of the palms and placed a foot in her hand, kicking back with her leg and leaning forward so her body approached horizontality. She then began a long discussion about the unseasonably warm weather and her hope that this was the real beginning of spring and not one of Sydney's characteristic late-August tricks.

I noticed she spoke with the slightest whistle, as though twisting the air when she talked, and I couldn't work out whether she was avoiding my eyes altogether or just shifting her gaze very regularly. I followed her stretching routine in a manner less exaggerated than hers, making sure my glutes, calves, quads, hip flexors and hamstrings got a sustained going-over. It only starts doing you good after thirty to forty-five seconds, she said, lose yourself in the stretch and make sure you spend a decent amount of time squatting, whether you're going for a run or not.

We did squats together in the trees for about two minutes, Coach steady as Buddha while I rocked, fell and readjusted. We shared in speculation about the weather and the way it intermixed with our hopes. Coach pointed to a sandy foot track that ran alongside the fence, up over the slope past the Cottage, and we set off towards it at a steady pace. Centennial Park occupied a mystical place within my imagination for two reasons. It was one of a series of places in the inner city and eastern suburbs which replenished what I would later come to call my landscape needs. I had a theory my emotional equilibrium was set to the relatively open, sparsely populated bush landscapes of the central west of New South Wales, where I spent the first part of life and where my family lived on a sheep and cattle farm. In order to settle myself in a place I needed to regularly move through an open landscape of abundant and varied vegetation. Centennial Park was one of the few places I had discovered close to the city which catered to this need. I also associated the park and its broader surrounds with my ex-girlfriend Alex, who was the source of some emotional baggage. I had never been to Alex's family home, but I knew she grew up near the park and her parents and younger brother still lived there. The house's indeterminate location meant that the whole area seemed to be haunted by a residue of vague yet intense emotions.

Coach Fitz's running tours opened up a new side of the park and our conversation sharpened my dawning analytical awareness of what I required of a city in order to be happy in it. I began to appreciate the distinctiveness of the different areas of vegetation and the atmospheres peculiar to certain arrangements of tree, rock outcrop, land gradient and ground cover. On our first run through Centennial, she drew my attention to important but easy-to-ignore elements of the landscape, such as the dune-like whitish sand patchily covered by grass, the scattered stringybarks and large pines, the needles of which created a bedding over the sand, and the marshy area populated by casuarinas, melaleucas, wattles and straw-like tufts of hardy grass and rushes.

Calling out to me over her shoulder as we ran, Coach said that she had developed an appreciation for wooded grasslands that featured this ratio of trees to open space, particularly when the ground is reliably dry and you hear its crackle under footfall. We passed a group of young runners in uniform and cut inwards towards to a copse of pines clustered on a small hill. Note the sand, yelled Coach, the persisting index of a past world!

We crossed a bridge over an inlet, then a grassy field, before heading up a small, steepish rise into another cluster of pines where the land levelled out. This area, said Coach, has always had the feel of the sacred about it. I'm not sure what it is, but the light always seems as though it is filtered. There's a sense that we're inside something, some ancient but invisible room.

We passed another entrance to the park and stuck close to the fence line. For the next couple of kilometres we ran through a gauntlet of Moreton Bay figs, their roots a web of tripwires in the sandy soil and their great low horizontal branches stretching over the track and the fence.

We crossed another grassy section before meeting up with the sealed road, and began a steady climb. At a break in the trees Coach pointed to a pavilion, a domed structure to which I'd never paid much attention. We passed a few other runners on the climb and as the gradient began to plateau I looked over my shoulder to see the pavilion through the trees sitting like a UFO from ancient Rome in the fields and in the foreground an amphitheatre, its white-caramel sandstone steps and trim grass empty and immaculate.

Coach slowed her pace a little so we were level. She appreciated the same reference point in the landscape, looked at my legs and then directly into my eyes, speaking in a deeper, gravelly voice, showing her teeth a little: How much weight we assign to the arts of the body is a decision of consequence; do not be tempted to imagine the figure you are is the one you must be! Witness the radiance in my body – she grabbed my t-shirt and pulled me in close while we still shuffled along together – answer the call of your legacy! Run with me and run like the wind!

The rest of the run was completed in an uncomfortable silence. The smooth trunks of a dense, small forest of Sydney blue gums and even the run down the open, grassy slope along the Lang Road fence – which in the years to come would be among my favourite parts of the course – did little to reignite our discussion. We parted with a lacklustre wave. Back at the Robinson Road gates, Coach, much like myself, seemed to be very much elsewhere after her outburst.

It took some time for the unsettling effect of Coach's exhortation to subside. I spent the drive home trying to imagine how I would put up with being regularly subject to such forceful and oddly grim eruptions of enthusiasm. I felt the still-resonant force of her grip, and touched the place on my chest where her knuckles had pressed.

Yet my trepidation was streaked with a grain of some other sentiment, a sense of having touched the real, to apply an expression I'd used on other occasions when in contact with a certain kind of intensity. I turned on the radio to be greeted by the opening riffs of 'Lazy Eye' by the Silversun Pickups. I scanned back through the images of Coach Fitz that had left an impression during our run. I could see her running just in front of me, feet picking through the exposed roots of trees and kicking up sand. She floated and led me onwards, quickening and slowing, her body loose and yet coiled like a spring at the same time.

She turned to face me and ran backwards, her hands in a slightly syncopated rhythm with the music in the car. She danced as though making staccato gestures of greeting, as though she was holding a large sphere in front of her body, palms turned inward on the diagonal, wrists exposed, shifting backwards and forwards, as though she was convincing me of something that couldn't be said in words.

I nodded my head to the music in the car, tapping the wheel and occasionally taking my hands off to mirror the moves of Coach Fitz.

After our first meeting Coach Fitz sent me an email that included an account of her training philosophy: a dynamic relationship between exercise of controlled intensity and a sense of steadily growing curiosity about places, buildings, aesthetics and history. Instead of the road races I'd envisaged for competition, Coach suggested the ambitious goal of the Six Foot Track trail marathon in March next year. The Six Foot Track followed an old bridle trail from Katoomba in the Blue Mountains to the Jenolan Caves, a place where one of Coach's favourite architects, Walter Liberty Vernon, built an impressive wilderness retreat in the late nineteenth century. Coach said there was no more fitting way to finish a gruelling trail run than to descend into the natural amphitheatre in which Caves House spread its multi-winged, four-storey form, commendably styled in the Arts and Crafts fashion.

Coach proposed a vague but adaptable running program we could flesh out with detail as our relationship progressed. Initially she suggested we meet on a weekly basis and go on a relaxed long

run together to discuss my progress and commitment. In addition
to this she would send me emails elaborating on the key points from
our discussions and suggested activities for the week. In exchange
I would complete her physical and mental exercises and document
the outcomes.

I immediately began thinking about how this program would
change my life and how I would make the necessary savings to fund
the small indulgence it involved. I began to direct my daily efforts
and daydreaming to the possibility of a future me that was faster on
foot, sensitive to the environment and mentally resilient. I would
take on extra work. I would wash windows of city department stores
and large eastern-suburbs houses from 6 a.m. until lunch, and in
the afternoons, from 3 until 6, I would supervise the activities of
primary school students on large playing fields in the suburb of Rose
Bay. I would take a job working at the cocktail bar of a restaurant in
Double Bay on Fridays and Saturdays, and when the lease finished
on the place I was renting in Balmain I would save more money by
fulfilling the long-held dream of living in my car, an early-model
maroon Honda Odyssey with a column-shift automatic gearbox
and back seats that folded into the floor, creating a large flat area on
which I could sleep. I would keep my clothes, toiletries and books
in the car and would use the outdoor showers of places such as
Redleaf Pool and North Bondi Beach to refresh myself between jobs
and in the mornings.

Throughout the day I would eat fresh vegetables such as green
runner beans and capsicums, bread, cheese, nuts, and fruit, favouring
exceptional bakeries such as Iggy's in Bronte, Sonoma in Five Ways

and Brickfields in Chippendale. After buying a loaf I would repeat the phrase *you can't cut corners on bread* to myself, in confirmation I'd done the right thing.

At night I would eat the leftovers from the day, have dinner with friends, or on the odd occasion treat myself to a meal out. I would develop a strong sense of gratitude for the mobile, secure space afforded by my car. The experience would be largely enlivening, though there would be trying moments, such as when I discovered a huntsman spider was living in the car and I couldn't manage to locate and remove it, or when the light and activity on a particular street at night made for a restless night's sleep.

The best thing would be waking with the sun and taking myself straight to a nearby bakery and then to head back to the ocean, the rock platform at the north end of Tamarama for example, to swim and watch the dogs socialise while I ate my bread, olive oil and tomatoes with the rising sun. On such mornings I would repeat any number of phrases to myself, affirming the blessed nature of my existence: You live a charmed life, heaven on earth, it doesn't get much better, *how good?*

Due to the savings in rent, the roll of fifty-dollar notes that I hid behind the ashtray in my car became fatter and fatter. Each time I met Coach Fitz I would peel off a number of these for her to stash away in her pocket.

During this time I learnt more and more about Coach Fitz and the techniques she used in her training programs. These addressed the desire to achieve modest athletic results in the context of some broader what one might call *lifestyle* ambitions of a more enduring nature.

Coach saw running as a useful mechanism through which to live well. As a result my training program involved specific sites of historical and aesthetic interest in addition to physical exercise. She encouraged me to keep a running diary filled with scrupulous observations of different environments, as well as my physiological and psychological states as I passed through them.

A further quirk to Coach Fitz's methods was her emphasis on overcoming adolescence. She believed that for most twenty-year-olds, young men of today in particular, the difficulties of adolescence were never adequately addressed and subsequently overcome.

Often, said Coach, the residue of those dark and uncertain days would cling to her subjects and cause all kinds of warps in their understanding and their neurochemical equilibrium. This, she noted, resulted in legions of maladapted young people seeking satisfaction in goals that did not provide outcomes of lasting delight, psychological expansion or nourishment of the spirit. These students, said Coach Fitz, were frequently not fit to undertake the necessary mental routines and rhetorical techniques to undergo and express experiences of genuine compassion, logic and self-care. They had no ability to register or tap into the fortifying effects induced by a sense of gratitude and servility to long-term collective goals.

Initially I didn't quite appreciate the source of Coach Fitz's enthusiasm for this particular emphasis. Luckily I did have the kind of attitude that made me a willing subject and to her enigmatic methods I responded with respect and by waiting, with faith, for the exercises to do their good work over time.

As I reflect back on this early period of my training it becomes apparent to me that, rather than substitute my existing practices with an entirely new program, Coach Fitz sought to adapt the training programs and lifestyle I had already begun to develop, the potential of which she registered in the enthusiasm I had demonstrated in my initial emails and during our first meetings.

Her demand that I reflect on and document the training I currently employed forced me to recognise the potential of the techniques I had been perfecting over the years and to see them as a program of promise in their own right. This encouragement and soft discipline was coupled with less yielding, didactic pieces of advice relating to the maintenance of a robust, accommodating and detoxified psychology.

When I mentioned my vaguely conceived project to catalogue the public sporting and leisure amenities on the coastal fringes of the city, Coach suggested I send her a draft. I had made a list that included: cricket nets, ovals, aspects, public toilets, hidden alleyways, picnic spots, shelters and footbridges. But the most fully expanded of my focuses were the various outdoor gyms where I performed exercise routines involving push-ups, sit-ups, burpees, chin-ups, leg raises, dips, squats, frontal and lateral lunges, and other still-developing exercises for which I didn't yet have names.

The first of the outdoor gyms I decided to write about was the one at North Bondi, which represented something of a paradigm for Sydney. In my email I wrote of a synthesis of garishness and glamour, and bodies of a particularly expressive physicality, willing to test themselves and experiment with unconventional exercise routines and parade in a self-assured and sometimes aggressive manner. There were the well-worn, developed, leathery bodies of those who had long practised at the gym, and the smoother, paler, emergent muscular figures of those newly attracted to the idea they might come to be the physical manifestation of an ideal they had deemed desirable for a range of variously agreeable and disagreeable reasons.

The equipment had been renewed over the years and now featured a composite rubber base and structural elements made from white-painted wood and stainless steel, marked with the grease of those struggling to deliberately inflict minor tears in their muscles and to inflate biceps, lats or pectorals with blood.

The North Bondi outdoor gym is also the site of an extreme case of territorial marking, I wrote to Coach Fitz. One of the regulars there pointed me to a severed ponytail tied high up on the nearby lamppost with duct tape. This, she said, is the remnant of a legend involving a turf war between a Brazilian and a Russian man. The Brazilian could juggle soccer balls for hours on end, while the Russian dedicated a good portion of his day to climbing as fast as he could up a five-metre-long rope at Ben Buckler Point. Apparently, there was once a plaque at the gym demarcating the area as belonging to the Russian because he used to spend so much time there working on his body. This displeased the Brazilian man, who defaced the plaque. Upon discovering this, the Russian suggested the Brazilian replace the plaque. His reluctance to accede to this demand provoked the Russian man to cut off the Brazilian's ponytail and tape it to the lamppost.

In my email to Coach Fitz I combined the details of this story with a personal account of the great variety of weather conditions and moods that tinted my experience of that particular site. Face down, holding my body in a steady plank on the protective rubber surface as the cool winds of the south replaced the warmer, heavier air of a mid-November day, squeezing in that last couple of tricep dips in the startling clarity of an early autumn morning, and sheltering from the summer heat in the shade provided by the scraggly remnant bitou bush, which had a variety of kettlebells secured to a series of lockable bike chains wrapped around its trunks, I speculated about what other items of recreation or leisure might be distributed in a similar fashion in other outdoor locations around the city, allowing certain clandestine communities to pursue diverse practices more commonly undertaken in private space.

I composed my email carefully. I enjoyed the task of sorting my messy thoughts into abstract, systematic sentences designed to induce a sense of sympathy and reverence in Coach Fitz. In the background of my thoughts was the harangue Coach inflicted upon me during our initial run: why hadn't I responded favourably to her address, despite her sentiments roughly aligning with my own ideas about the physical arts and overcoming the improbable through systematic self-transformation? Perhaps my contemporaries had conditioned me to a point where I expected information to be diluted by irony, particularly when it came to athletic ambition?

Free from such undertones, Coach's voice sounded alien, robotic, impossible to trust due to the purity and force of its conviction.

As I read back through my email, I tried to get a measure of its tone. I thought about the rare occasions when I had discovered a friend not only willing to hear my efforts to bring my discriminatory faculties to bear on something as ordinary as gym equipment, but keen to see these faculties develop. I did have a friend in high school called Patricia, who I knew could be relied upon for fine-grained analysis on the topics of confectionery, biscuits, and chips, and for a short time we collaborated on a complex rating system which we planned to publish in a zine. However, in response to such activities, my friends and family would typically make quips, or tilt their heads, and use expressions like *wow, really* and *tell me more,* lacing their phrases with traces of irony small enough to maintain a language game that would exclude the overly earnest or enthused. The great promise Coach Fitz offered was that she would be a companion who would not deactivate the energy of my expressions with cool remarks, and would even provide the kind of guidance that would open out new experiences and systems from my existing preoccupations.

Meeting Two: Cooper Park

For our second meeting Coach Fitz suggested a run through and around Cooper Park in Bellevue Hill, which I previously knew only as an obscure lump of bush, viewed inadequately from the gallery of the surrounding roads through my car windscreen.

We met in the late afternoon at the top of the large set of sandstone stairs on Victoria Road, which Coach Fitz noted was often a site of pilgrimage for runners around the area wishing to build muscle strength in their quads or for people who simply enjoyed the view across the bushland and Woollahra to the harbour and the city beyond.

We stretched at the stone pillars, Coach Fitz emphasising the importance of developing an appreciation for stretching as an event as important as the run itself, and an ability to take control of what she referred to as 'dead time' and use it as a source for contemplation, pleasure, or to simply take it on its own terms in a fashion free from agitation.

While we stretched Coach Fitz drew my attention to the unique features of the site, commenting on her love of natural amphitheatres, of which this was a fine example, and on her deliberate choice to embark on the run at a time when the transition from day to night was experienced to its fullest extent. Coach said that the feeling of running through an amphitheatre gave her the sense of being watched over and spurred on by the landscape. It accommodated the degree of theatricality she believed was crucial to activate in the soul of a runner. The world is watching you, she would say, run like the wind!

We set off at a relaxed pace down the steps, the cape of Coach Fitz's hat flapping lightly as she ran. We crossed a flat area of lush green before meeting with some boggy turf, and then moved on to a sandstone path that snaked its way down to meet a stream. Classic Sydney wet sclerophyll, Coach noted, as we began the descent into the cooler, darker, wetter understorey at the upper end of the gully.

Coach continued to yell questions, observations and anecdotes back over her shoulder as we ran. She asked disarmingly brash questions about my self-image and my history that would have made me uncomfortable were I not moving through bushland at pace. While I was haltingly formulating a reply, Coach pointed northwards and began a story involving an athlete that, like a number of her students, had come to her bearing the late-adolescent burden of acne. He would sit in his car before a date near a thickly treed verge, Coach said, turning his face this way and that in the rear-view mirror, engaging in a fraught and meticulous effort to conceal his flaws with an ill-chosen hue of foundation he had been reduced to buying from a well-lit chemist. This boy came to me having already astutely identified the problem he would ask me to solve, continued Coach. He told me that he didn't want to become his affliction, he didn't want to turn to disinhibiting substances that enabled him to forget about the persistent lumpy pains in his face and so exacerbate the problem. Instead, he wanted to find a way to inhabit the psychological ambience of an idealised figure from the future that would look back on this condition and see it only as a fleeting issue.

I went on many runs around this park with that boy, said Coach, and we established a resilient and life-giving set of delusions that he employed in the rehabilitation of his damaged self-image. And this, this is what I mean to offer you.

Coach spoke in a manner that made me feel she didn't require answers from me at that time, but that she nonetheless knew the story would be directly relevant to most subjects of my generation who sought out her help. There were answers I was waiting to give, answers that told of my previous desires to rapidly become a man, to prove my worth as a human through effortless displays of this manliness, and to distance myself from the smooth-skinned, slim-shouldered, fragile thing that scuttled about his high school gym, gradually adding weights to the bench press and dumbbells.

As we ran further into what Coach described as the bowels of Cooper Park, the luminous late afternoon dimmed to a shadowy green gloom that seemed to correspond perfectly with the gritty smell of wet rocks and moss. I felt insulated in a pocket of shadow that seemed a different world from the one I'd left only moments ago. Before me, like an escaped wheel of cheese tumbling down a rough slope, Coach skimmed over the ground cracked and rippled with raised rocks and roots, speeding up at the moments where I'd expect someone to slow, using the contours of the ground to adjust her pace, quickening into the darkness then re-emerging, a mirage that carried the light mothball smell of my father's jumpers and whose breathing was barely detectable above footfall and the light trickle of water down the gully. Coach ran like a boxer or a dancer.

We kept a straight course and left the paved sandstone path for a wet, uneven dirt trail. Coach would later tell me that it was key to keep the feet dancing with minor obstacles, and that on some days we might even go on runs along rocky headlands or thistle-ridden ground to ensure my feet and eyes together moved faster than my thinking.

The path met a set of stairs and led us out into a clearing and over a brick bridge, the stonework of which Coach described as modest but exemplary. To the left was a squat terracotta-roofed red-brick toilet. I heard the distinctive, reassuring thwacks of tennis balls meeting tennis racquets, and looked ahead to see a row of courts lit up by the recently activated overhead lights. The dusk of one day and the dawn of another, said Coach, drawing my attention to the inverted synchronicity of new light emerging as the light of the day faded.

We ran along the concrete path to the right of the tennis courts. I was intrigued to see this collection of radiant, white-clothed individuals submitting themselves to the rules and confines of their chosen game, secluded in the womb of the bush.

Coach reflected on the 'chapters' of Cooper Park, and how the paths can take you from busy road to grass field to bush trail to recreational structure, each with its own mood.

We left the glowing air of the tennis courts and jogged through a car park before meeting a large grassy strip banked by dense, overgrown scrub on one side and populated by the early evening's dog walkers. As we ran across the field some of the bolder dogs joined us and ran alongside for a short while, and I watched Coach accelerate to test their enthusiasm before they peeled off in obedience to the receding whistles of their owners.

We passed cricket nets with players packing up their kit in the day's dimming light, hurdled a low wooden fence, crossed a sealed road enclosed in the darkness of Moreton Bay figs, and met with yet another series of playing fields, these bordered on the left by a sloping lawn that transitioned to lantana and large sandstone rocks beneath the worlds-away privacy of dark backyards and well-lit interiors.

Coach had surged ahead on this grassy flat, so I called on my reserves to make sure I didn't miss any of the advice she was doling out over her shoulder. We re-entered the streetscape at the far edge of the fields and ran on a quiet lane alongside a concrete canal.

I was familiar with this area of Double Bay from what I would later describe to Coach as my misspent years, and more recently from my stint as a cocktail waiter at a restaurant in the area. However, I had never experienced it from such an approach; our entry and exit from the park had been perfectly choreographed with the transition from day to night. The sense that I'd passed through multiple alternative worlds seemed to elongate time and refresh my sense of the city.

We turned right and began the ascent up Bellevue Road, which Coach noted as being a good length and gradient to get my legs adapted to the greater challenges of the Six Foot Track. We pulled up by the sandstone gates at the top of the stairs on Victoria Road, at which point, under Coach's orders, I began twenty gruelling repetitions up and down, working on my attitude at the same time as my quads. Coach stood leaning on one of the pillars, offering sometimes cryptic pieces of encouragement.

At the conclusion of the session I stretched with Coach at the top of the steps. We looked out over the tangle of bush to the city lights and the bright, grubby yellow cloud beyond.

The first aims of the runner, said Coach, ought to be to keep running, the foundation of which is to be injury-free. It is for this reason important not to lose sight of things like stretching, rest and hydration.

While I engaged in the combination of strain and relaxation peculiar to stretching, Coach made further inquiries about the next outdoor gym I planned to describe in an email.

I had composed a list of candidates, and ended up selecting the outdoor gym by the basketball courts in Prince Alfred Park, rather than the apparatus on the coastal walk from Bondi to Tamarama near Marks Park, or the equally tempting chin-up bars on the playing fields at Balmoral Beach.

As I explained to Coach in a more elaborate email later in the week, I chose the Prince Alfred gym because of the peculiar vantage it offered on the energy of the city, overlooking the railway lines that run between Redfern and Central stations. The combination of the proximity to the railway, the nearby basketball court and what could be described as a backstage view of the CBD conferred on the gym the sense that it was part of another city, maybe a naïve imagining of New York.

The park is also one of the landscapes close to the city that features an abundance of native grass, in this instance a motley, almost fleshy-coloured red-green-pale-yellow mass of kangaroo grass. From the right perspective, looking across from Cleveland Street, the kangaroo grass forms its own silhouette against the sky and, as I wrote to Coach Fitz in my email, it is easy to imagine that its tall stems would be a CBD of sorts to an insect.

It was on this equipment that I first used a fitness app on my phone, one that involved randomly selected playing cards. The cards acted as prompts to perform a specific number of repetitions of a given exercise, such as push-ups, squats or chin-ups. I used the app excitedly at first and then soon after stopped, preferring my own adaptable form of randomisation and trusting in the disciplining support of my athletic ingenuity.

It was here also that I witnessed some of the first outdoor exercise routines to awaken me to the possibilities of movement other than the mechanical, intensity-focused program I had tended to prefer. The most striking example of this was an elderly Chinese man outfitted in white shorts and t-shirt who performed rhythmic squat and hip-rotation exercises under the large Moreton Bay fig. The sense of care and enjoyment evident in his attitude offered me a reference point I could call on whenever I saw it necessary to introduce a diversity of mood into my routines. Coach Fitz was especially pleased to hear that I'd made a note of this serendipitous assistant, and expressed her familiarity with the park by referring to it under the much more appealing name of Cleveland Paddocks.

We finished our stretches in the dark at the stone gates of Cooper Park. When we parted, Coach said that our next meeting would be at a very special place for Sydney runners, Sir Joseph Banks Park. She also tentatively proposed a dinner or lunch, to give a different mood the chance to develop.

I told Coach that I knew of many great cafés in the inner west, to which she responded with a nod, while suggesting instead that the lobby of a hotel like the Medina or the Mercure might be more appropriate, where it was likely to be quieter and the food, she reassured me, was actually quite good. It is, I think you'll find it is.

Meeting Three: Sir Joseph Banks Park

At our meeting in Sir Joseph Banks Park Coach Fitz provided me with what she called a 'breath friend', which was something to be enunciated while exercising like a mantra. My breath friend would be *hick-a-chee*, she told me, as well as the related sequences *hick-a-chee hick-a-chee whaa* and *hick-a-chee hick-a-chee whaa-whaa-whaa*. Coach said it was my task to add detail and vivacity to the repertoire of feelings and images associated with this breath friend. Throughout the session I found it difficult to gauge the level of her seriousness, but based on the complete lack of irony in her communications so far I decided she was in earnest.

We stood near the characteristically busted-up-looking melaleuca on the grass verge outside the Sir Joseph Banks Hotel, which retained fine cast-iron filigrees that Coach noted were typical of buildings of that era.

Don't pressure yourself to produce too much stable and clear visual information about *hick-a-chee*, she said. It should remain a vague sense of something. Focus on familiarising yourself with the atmosphere that characterises the relationship between the two of you, basic but important things like the spatial arrangement of your bodies: does *hick-a-chee* stand before you, does it float, does it appear at your shoulder, is it a halo, is it accompanied by a vehicle or sidekick? Concentrate on the feeling associated with being in the presence of *hick-a-chee*. The voice and phrases you use in confrontation with it, any performative greetings, your disposition in its company. It's possible too, said Coach Fitz, that *hick-a-chee* might have various accomplices which come from your memory.

These you might be able to picture more clearly. We follow this procedure because all runners must run within a sacred chapel of their own creation.

Hick-a-chee, hick-a-chee, whaa, I said the words over in my head and felt the light sense of rhythm they induced in my breath. I immediately and somewhat regrettably called to mind the image of an amused golden Buddha draped in blue and grey-purple striped robes sitting atop a cloud. I shook my head compulsively, attempting to remove the thought, and asked Coach Fitz about how to rid myself of such generic imagery. She gave a counterintuitive bit of advice that I recall clearly to this day. Coach said it was best not to fight such temptations, as she had in the past, but to see them as evidence of the humour that defined my relationship with *hick-a-chee.*

We set off down a road that led behind the hotel to Sir Joseph Banks Park, the site of the first zoo in Sydney and some of the oldest recreational facilities in the city. These included a cinder athletics track that Coach described as having a very pleasing shape. The entrance to the park featured two bright blue pillars topped with the busts of a couple of panicked-looking horses painted green. Our warm-up encompassed the grassy parkland surrounding the old athletics track. A typical mix of melaleuca, Moreton Bay fig and casuarina grew along the edges of a swampy inlet. Not far off, over the edge of a grassy bank in the direction of the horizon, were the now-stilled giant blue-and-orange cranes of Port Botany. The persistent dim whir of the nearby airport provided a background to the occasional whisper of the wind through the casuarinas.

I thought of my youth, when the sound of aeroplanes cutting their yawns into the sky induced a pronounced feeling of melancholy within me. A feeling that the people on the plane were my friends and family, the special people of my life, on a journey to where I wanted to be, somewhere far away.

As we crisscrossed our way around the park at a steady pace Coach pointed me to the various sculptures of animals, including concrete bears, gorillas, tigers, and elephants made of corrugated iron and mesh, all of which were once housed in the park during its days as a zoo. In their petrified form the bears seemed by far the most peaceful, one in particular lounging in its bed of woodchips, face dappled in sunlight and shade. The tigers appeared nonchalant and noble, whereas the gorillas, like the horses, had a stressed and aggressive look.

We continued through the park, Coach floating over the turf about ten or so metres in front me, occasionally stepping sharply in one direction, as if dodging an invisible figure, then resuming her original trajectory.

A crew of rangers in fluoro vests was scanning the ground carrying sticks with little wire nooses on the end. Coach jogged over to one and motioned for me to join. A nest of Argentinian fire ants had recently been discovered in the area and the rangers were checking to ensure they hadn't spread any further. The ranger produced a small plastic case that contained a series of dead ants arranged horizontally from left to right in order of increasing size. She mentioned that the ants had a particularly nasty bite, and Coach Fitz concurred that the last thing we needed was another ant to rival the green ant, and that I ought to feel privileged to have been witness to such an array of preserved animals.

We jogged on, pausing to stretch on a circular tiled mosaic that depicted Banks' sea voyage to Australia. Coach mentioned that foot races were held at the track as far back as the 1880s during a golden age of sprint racing and the era of pedestrianism. One athlete in particular is worth calling to mind as we run around this track today, said Coach Fitz.

Charlie Samuels ran 134 yards in 12.3 seconds in this very spot in 1888, barefoot, complete with the nicotine and alcohol addiction that was one of the many gifts bestowed on his people after white settlement. Samuels lived for a while at a camp in Centennial Park, then moved to the Aboriginal reserve at La Perouse before being admitted to an insane asylum after an altercation with police, reportedly suffering from a mental disorder caused by ill health and love affairs.

He was apparently the ideal build for a runner, said Coach Fitz, slight upper body with lower legs like Achilles, a decent set of thighs and meaty bum. He finished his life back in Queensland, the place of his birth, his first wife and children dying of consumption in 1905 before he followed them with the same affliction seven years later.

In Charlie Samuels, said Coach Fitz, we see a classic example of what a substance can do to a life in the absence of cultural and personal routines adapted to dealing with its peculiar force. The way running worked in his life probably encouraged him to drink and smoke rather than acting as a force that restored health and emotional stability, not to mention the great sadness it was his burden to manage due to the destruction of his people's culture.

It takes many centuries even to partially adapt to the bizarre, often cruel practices of the white man, said Coach Fitz. Samuels' abilities were no doubt seen by so-called trainers as a means to amass wealth and entertain. The combination of alcohol, gambling and sporting spectacles is, Coach Fitz continued, an ugly alliance that continues to exert an often difficult to comprehend force over the population to this day.

The memory and stories of my own grandfather struck me directly and with an emotionally transformative purchase at this point. An all-schools champion over 100 and 200 yards, a hamstring injury he suffered had cruelly and prematurely ended an athletics career of great promise. He was thereby condemned to live in the shadow of the legend he might have become, and the thrill of the race was to some extent substituted by horseracing and booze. I could understand why it would have been hard for him to maintain the mundane training practices that in the long term might have brought further health and happiness to his life. Perhaps to him there would have been no point. The chance for glory in that realm had passed.

For my grandfather and the generations before, sport was to some extent about talent more than effort. The sublime athlete did not need to train – it was simply a matter of exercising a gift, rather than striving towards a perfect technique.

I looked at Coach Fitz and thought of her contrasting attitude to running – how it seemed as though to her an empty grandstand offered as much promise as a full one, as though an entourage of diverse motivators accompanied her wherever she went, sculpted with effort from history, memory and imagination, allowing her soul to confer with them during moments of boredom or duress.

I did sets, first one lap, then two, three, four, then back down to three, two and one, with Coach Fitz egging me on from the sideline. The experience was permeated by fanciful thoughts and feelings relating to the two very different, yet in that context somehow compatible, histories of my grandfather and Charlie Samuels. I recalled the fragmentary bits of advice my grandfather had given me before athletics carnivals as a primary school student: pick a spot behind the finish line and run through the line towards it.

I let my body tilt like a gnomon around the bends, the dirt grinding lightly under my bare feet, and as I entered the straight the tight curve of the track seemed to spur me forwards just that little bit faster as I ran through the line, that invisible though compelling spatial boundary, pulling up each time well after I'd crossed.

Coach would complete some sets running alongside me, while on others she would wait at the finish line to observe. Before the last lap I noticed Coach looking upwards and away as though to some distant corner of the sky. I puzzled for a while at whether this unusual gesture was meant to direct me in some way, or whether it was a product of her tense introspection.

As I rounded the first bend on the last lap and felt the absence of energy in my muscles, I noticed what was at first the faintest trace of a voice in my breathing. My realisation crystallised and the voice became more pronounced. Ah, I heard myself saying, you have come, *hick-a-chee*. Ah, *hick-a-chee*, you haven't left me, you are still there. And my grandfather, Charlie Samuels and *hick-a-chee* sailed through the finish line together buoyed by a feeling of purpose, lightness and ecstasy that I would come more and more to experience in those early days with Coach Fitz.

That night I treated myself to a meal out and a couple of beers. I purchased some takeaway food from a favourite Indian restaurant on Parramatta Road and some fragrant beers from the bottle-o nearby. I then drove to Jubilee Park and flipped the back seats in the Odyssey over so I could sit with my legs dangling out the back of the car and eat my dinner looking across the park to Blackwattle Bay.

I consulted my most vivid thoughts from the day, and wondered more about the way athletics had functioned in the life of my grandfather, and about his modest efforts to inculcate an awareness and appreciation for this pastime in his progeny. I thought about the inscription he'd written in the front page of a book, written by one of Australia's most successful authors, which featured an account of his high school athletic achievements, and about his emphasis on genes being passed from his father down the line – a framing of things clearly influenced by his post-athletic career as an agricultural scientist.

Included also in the book was a clipping from a 1929 newspaper that included a description of his father's sporting ability, my great-grandfather, a lad of seventeen with an athletic build, a strong and speedy runner with plenty of determination who excelled in rugby games at places like Wentworth Oval and Wiley Park, and who was all-schools champion over 100 and 320 yards. According to the article, his qualities were in turn inherited from his father, the most spectacular and successful cyclist in the western districts of New South Wales.

My imagination was ignited by the fantasy of certain shared qualities persisting through time, and I thought about the extent to which story-making played a role in the activation of abilities and characteristics. My own athletic abilities were middling, clearly not directly inherited from my grandfather, but I still delighted in my proximity to this family history and the chance to imagine my grandfather extending himself in sporting competitions. I called on his presence when my own body was in motion around a grass track or on the finishing stretch of a taxing run along tar.

The genes I did seem to inherit directly from my grandfather were instead perhaps a predisposition to stress – a forewarning about which would have played a beneficial role in my life maintenance – and a unique family grimace that was displayed in concert with feelings of inadequacy and frustration when minor tasks, such as retrieving cups from a cupboard or packing things in the freezer, were not completed with grace.

In this moment, in good part influenced by the lessons of the day with Coach Fitz, I decided on one of the principles that would be key to the training practice I would some day like to share with younger athletes: that athletics and sport ought to be regarded as practices that allow the transformation of self and an immunising response to stress rather than repeated victory over others.

In reflecting on this distinctively paternal mapping of ancestry from the back seat of the Odyssey, I felt it was necessary to deal with a further issue that I'd also found myself confronting during the lead-up to my grandfather's funeral. When my grandmother had passed away less than a year earlier, I found myself lacking inspiration when it came to the time to say something at her funeral about the resonant feelings she'd passed on to me with regard to my ambitions and sympathies. My sister took the baton for the grandchildren and spoke compellingly of lessons she took from my grandmother, a meditation on her warm but direct character, which was manifest in the searing judgements she might offer on the prospective partners of her daughters and granddaughter.

When my grandfather died, in the summer after that winter, I immediately felt a set of ideas and life lessons readied within me that would form the basis of a remembrance at his funeral: most centrally, his enduring love of games and of constructing rules to approximate perfect conditions of fairness through systems of handicapping – from my youth when he offered support for my younger brother if I was excelling too much in a game of cricket, or in the mock war games involving dried thistle stalks and sheep poo. Right up until my life as an adult, he was driven by a desire to create the conditions of fairness that would allow for the most intense competition. He would spend what must have been a decent portion of the year working out appropriate teams and rules for the ever more elaborate 'Olympics' that occupied an increasingly important position during our Christmas Day festivities: a combination of artfully assembled quizzes, with questions drawn from various newspapers and matched evenly to the talents of his various children and grandchildren, as well as a gruelling and diverse series of athletic events, ranging from driveway sprints and longer paddock runs, to projectile and target-based games.

Although I knew about certain disagreeable elements of his character, my grandfather was without doubt a prominent agent in my imagination. By contrast, my grandmother was a comparatively passive, if reassuring, presence. The same was the case for my other sets of grandparents and great-grandparents, with the paternal voices cajoling me into action, or offering an example with whom I could engage in an imagined dialogue when confronted with uncertainty about what kind of a character I was among all the other characters in the world, while the maternal figures remained relatively passive in my upbringing, associated with feelings of great warmth during childhood, but fading to a dimmer influence as my agency increased. This trend seemed to stop with my own parents, where it becomes difficult for me to say who is more or less an agent in my memory and imagination.

As I made the best efforts to mop up the last of the aloo baingan from the container I habitually used for my takeaway meals, I was satisfied my own progeny, should they someday manifest, would take equal measure of inspiration from the activities of their paternal grandparents and this would, with any luck, come to be the norm for generations to come.

Soft Sands and Headlands, Manly to Dee Why and Back
For our next run Coach suggested we meet in the suburb of Manly, which she described as a more rustic, less ethnically diverse version of Bondi.

It is a site, said Coach Fitz, that meets with an idealised vision of Australia held by a large portion of overseas tourists, particularly those from the United Kingdom and Brazil. Nearby is the beach where the first surfing in Australia took place, and the suburb is still to a large degree defined by surf culture.

I often meditate on the differences between Sydney's two iconic beaches, said Coach, and I tend to end up at the conclusion that Manly is less glamorous and eccentric, more parochial and in some vague sense more honest, or at least its inhabitants might have such aspirations. I've thought of Bondi as disco and Manly as rock-and-roll, though I'm not entirely happy with the analogy.

We met at the southern end of the beach for a session of 'soft sands and headlands', in Coach's words, up to the northern end of Dee Why, before turning to retrace the same path south, potentially doing four repetitions of Curl Curl Beach along the way, depending on our enthusiasm.

Coach warned me that it would be a more taxing run than our recent efforts, but the sands according to her belief were an important part of this first phase of our training: an ideal way to clock up distance on the legs, increase stability, and build core strength without the jarring effects of bitumen.

The beach was a beehive of activity at 7.30 a.m., with body after body emerging from the shallows like some amphibious subspecies, many sheathed in rubber suits and caps they peeled off and discarded near the outdoor showers. The chat among the participants was animated by the vitality the exercise brought to their bodies, and Coach was quick to point out that this was an exemplary institution featuring a great variety of body shapes and ages. I had a vision of her walking over to one of the specimens in the manner of a documentary presenter, prodding the girth of a grey-haired man while continuing to talk earnestly to the camera.

We left our towels near the steps that led down to the sand and set off shuffling along, Coach instructing me to focus on small steps and balance. I kept an eye on her gait and attempted to follow her cadence.

As we battled through the early stages, during which our bodies were still waking up to the idea of a run, Coach offered the view that humans often display the unfortunate tendency of equating their heads with the centres of their body. This makes for a terrible running style and a wilted running spirit, she said. The body's orienting centre is for starters not simply located in any particular spot. It shifts about in the manner of a gas or a liquid. When I run, said Coach Fitz, I often think of my pelvis as the driving engine that orients the rest of my body. But this changes. I create imperatives in my immediate past that direct my running in the present, through running at different speeds and according to different sentiments, engagements with my surrounds and other internal conversations. I entertain myself at each point and consider every run to be an adventure. It is easy to forget this while training in continuous circles, back and forth along the beach or up and down hills.

I watched Coach alternate between a wider and narrower stance, her steps always small and deliberate. There was a sense that she was fooling around, often attacking a softer lump of sand with intent, ploughing up a bank, slowing to run almost on the spot.

We hit the stairs at the north end, ran up over the hill and down the flights and ramps on the other side to Freshwater. I always love the stairs down to Freshy, said Coach, it's often warmer here because it cops a good dose of the morning sun, there are nice plant smells, always a bird or two piping up and nasturtiums networking in clipped shrubs.

As we hopped through the rocks at the north end of the beach, up past the toilets and along the path to Curl Curl, Coach began to lecture me on what she saw as one of the key transition stages for people of my age and gender. People think adolescence ends during high school, she said, that there aren't any transition stages beyond those years, things simply happen to them or the changes are experienced blindly. For a lot of men, the hormones in their body leave them with the sense that what makes life worth living is the possibility that anything is a possibility. They devise countless ceremonies for this. At its worst the 'anything goes' attitude can become a cheap trick to make people feel power. If you always allow yourself the possibility that you might do worse, might always be more unpredictable, you retain an element of surprise and therefore power. Our culture is designed to fuel the more or less haphazard, more or less routinised quest for transcendence that significant portions of this demographic favour. Then a point comes when the old routine is shaded by uncertainty, lacking reliable fulfilment, and you don't know where to look for meaning. You react, seeking increasingly extreme measures, or succumbing to the enveloping sense of sadness, lack of purpose and frustration. We should have a name for this phase too, as though adolescence were the first and last of our transitions!

I puzzled at what Coach said. The idea that I was somehow implicated in her narration provoked a strong negative reaction. I submitted the idea to close scrutiny, fuelled primarily by a forceful disbelief which turned out to be transient. While it was difficult to admit at the time, another part of me stored away her advice to consult in the future and inflict on others to whom I felt it relevant.

We snaked along the concrete path, which met with a wooden boardwalk that led down through a car park to Curl Curl, the ocean to our right looking slate-blue and menacing.

What's the alternative, I said, things don't strike me as so bad, isn't routinised transcendence what we're after, here, right now?

Coach thought on this a while as we followed the slope down to soft sand. The rocks at the south end are particularly exposed at the moment, she said – but instead of slowing to pick her way through them carefully she met them at pace, feet knifing up and down, springing from edge to edge.

The sand was noticeably softer than Manly or Freshwater and we ploughed on up the beach with a light tailwind and Coach's hat flapping. It's about not knowing how to ritualise transformation, she said. Adolescence is just perceived as this problematic, disagreeable thing that arrives and then stops. There is a lack of felicitously disseminated foreknowledge of the changes you are likely to meet. What I reckon happens is that young men don't recognise they need to transform in order to live well. Worse still, the older generations often pander to this juvenile sensibility to maintain contact with what they perceive as their own lost vitality. We don't equip young people with the practices that could unfold at the right times, and it creates this horrible mess. We're raising generations of man-children who suckle on entertainment as a mild source of amusement and protect themselves with a profound but often unacknowledged commitment to an insipid variety of irony. People can't control themselves adequately. They have no sense of practice, or they choose unsustainable practices. The only saviours are accidental: things like babies and death wake some up, but that won't do, it only stuns a small few into action and the rest it makes worse.

What's your alternative? I asked again, as I kept an eye on Coach's gait, ensuring my steps remained small and my body upright.

We need to be selective and clever in the examples we offer to men when they're between fourteen and twenty-seven. At the very least they need a decent sex education. This is where I position my coaching services. I see coaching athletics as a way of creating the whole person, including the sexual person. It's about making the probable pitfalls explicit so you are ready for the future and don't simply react or fall prey to instincts or inheritance. To me it seems pretty mathematical: effort equals reward, but we've got the machines, drugs or autistic fantasies doing too much of the work for us. Something from nothing is what we expect. That's one side of it. The other part is lacking rituals that take in the full scope of human feeling and intelligence.

I remained reluctant to see myself as a symptom of the broader cultural problems Coach had identified, but the practical possibilities of self-improvement through her approach were promising, and I reflected on how convenient it would be to transmit this knowledge back through time so I could receive it before the end of my relationship with Alex – though perhaps the only way to do this in reality was to open up about my past failings and share my memories of that period with Coach herself.

The stairs past the surf club at the north end were closed, so we went up the ramp and onto the bush track. I love this first incline, said Coach, such nice variability, roots and rocks, enclosures and openings, thanks to the stunted shrubs, trees and decent-sized rocks. The next few ups and downs are just as good.

As we rounded the other side of the headland we hit another pocket of warm air and our feet met with rivulets from the watering of the backyards above. A few stretches featured metal railings and wooden pathways, and sometimes the path cut deeper into the low shrubs, vine and rock, so we were two torsos bobbing along above the bushes. Sometimes it was a hands-and-feet job to scale the ledges.

There's plenty of dancing to be done, said Coach. We crept up on a couple of runners wearing iPods who, Coach exclaimed, were incarnations of the reliance on self-insulation and mood-management tools people now require in order to act. Her blanket antagonism to frivolity, combined with her almost manic apologies to these runners for our stealing up on them, provoked the first trace elements of disdain in me that would gradually come to prevent me from receiving her advice well in our future dialogues.

We emerged from the bush above Dee Why and kept a steady pace past the ocean pool and its surrounding amenities. Like at Curl Curl the sand here was soft, but taking on a more orange tinge, a transition Coach noted as defining the journey along the Northern Beaches.

We kept to a levelled bit of ground worn by previous runners up on the far, dry edge of the beach. Coach was doing it easy, while I noticed the first dark patches of sweat coming through my t-shirt. We quickened our pace up the headland at the north end, past the golf course where dogs and humans socialised on their morning walks. At the top we used the vigorous bubbler installed there, and spent a few moments taking in the 270-degree sea view.

Slate-grey clouds were now spreading out to engulf the sky back to the south over Manly. Looks grim, said Coach, but don't let it take the wind out of your sails. That's an hour and ten kilometres done, she said. We headed back along the same route, stopping at a mixed business for a nut bar and a drink at the south end of Dee Why.

The folk getting about at Dee Why were a more motley gathering than at Manly, with the kinetically atypical, and others just a bit rough around the edges, well represented. Coach confirmed that from Manly northwards, until you hit maybe Newport, the health of the population gradually drifts from optimal to average, while diversity of background, income and cultural heritage tends to increase.

I really felt the lactic acid in my quads along Curl Curl on the way back, particularly with the headwind pushing against me. Coach was making barely audible sounds mixed in with her breathing: *he-he ha, he-he ha*, attacking the sand with her feet.

We finished up back at South Steyne, stopping for a dip as light rain began to fall. A total of twenty kilometres in two hours, me with very shaky legs. Coach made an immediate and clumsy entry into the water, half-tripping half-diving into the shallows with her hat on before standing and producing a soft plastic ball she must have tucked into her underwear. We stood a short way apart in the shallows and skimmed the ball between us until my legs were numbed by the water.

We discussed our favourite meat pie fillings and whether the water on the north coast of New South Wales was different to that of the south. Coach commented that each beach orchestrates a meeting of sand and water, a certain mood or consistency, according to the arrangement of sandbars, light, temperature and outcrops of rock.

I don't know what to call the way you gauge the feeling of surrounding water on your face, she said, while you're swimming within it – its peculiar tastes and consistency against your skin and how the pressure differential between what's inside and outside your head impacts on your thoughts.

Looking back now, I watch the unpainted, unphotographed scene that emerged between us, two figures in the shallows hurling a ball back and forth for eternity, knowing, somehow, that we were creating the future with our custom.

Drying ourselves at the top of stairs, facing out to graduations of a blue and building swell, Coach inspected me up and down and asked what kind of body I desired.

The last time I had considered this question in an explicit and programmatic fashion was during my high school years, where I sought to replace my lack of bulk with muscle in the areas deemed to accentuate masculinity, eventually acquiring a decent set of pectorals, biceps, and the regrettable nickname Paddy McArms –

but since then I hadn't given it a lot of thought, and I told Coach as much.

She pondered this at length, her short legs bent at the knees as though ready to leap, arms held at her sides like those of a kangaroo or velociraptor. She rapped me in the abdominals with the back of her knuckles and I cringed to shield myself from further attacks. I see, she continued, that you have acquired a beautiful set of pectorals and a pleasingly ripped, V-shaped torso. However, the program that has given form to your body up to this point has significant limitations. The image you've used to guide your training lacks dynamism, it's too dependent on inherited ideas to do with visual appeal and not grounded in a notion of strength informed by adaptability of movement. We will make you more animal, she said, in an accent that seemed slightly Russian, though I couldn't be sure. This is the next stage for your body, the animal. The animal is the ultimate and most encompassing of prototypes towards which human ideas of fitness must aspire. Once you have mastered both the animal and the plant you are equipped to maintain psychosomatic equilibrium even in conditions utterly hostile to vitality.

Internet Café

I spent that evening in my favourite internet café on Bondi Road, the atmospherics of which I found conducive to a better internet experience than looking at my smartphone in the back of the Odyssey. I enjoyed the feeling I was a tourist visiting my own city. I liked the greasy keyboard, being surrounded by the bright, intensely flavoured packages of food and drink, the harsh lighting and the smell of dampness mixed with a sweet, synthetic fragrance which I attributed to the box of killer pythons at the counter.

The ambience of the café activated certain memories of an overseas trip, which I intensified by looking at photographic records of my travels while listening to music through my earphones, a practice that now seemed complicated by Coach's views on mood management, and their disagreement with the pleasures I had habitually enjoyed in the past. I couldn't quite get a handle on the logic at work in her championing of direct, unmediated, sensory immersion in the world, particularly when she seemed quite partial to the pleasures of newspapers and phones when it suited her.

I was joined by a young woman in thongs and an Irish rugby jersey, who poked away at the keyboard of the computer next to me with one hand, while in the other she held a gradually deteriorating ice cream. I thought about Coach's comments about adolescence in relation to my own efforts some years prior to escape a feeling of hopelessness that had begun to inform my experience of Sydney. A certain effervescence associated with my initial years in the city had dissipated, and I had begun to seek sustenance in the idea of an overseas trip, the visual evidence of which I now reviewed with melancholy ecstasy under the influence of my favourite songs by the London dubstep artist Burial.

I wondered whether I should write an email to Coach about my experiences overseas and the formative emotional challenges that I encountered during my journey; about the failed romance, and what I now saw as a lack of robustness and diversity in my practices of exercise and knowledge production. Something in me resisted the idea, as I felt it would give her yet more authority and put me in a position of greater vulnerability. I sensed a tension between two seemingly incompatible urges, to disclose and to protect myself, which gave texture to my experience as I looked at the rare, much-viewed photographs on Facebook of my time in London with Alex.

Certain images took on a strangeness that made me question their status as fragments of a life I had actually lived. They seemed more like covers to the magazines in my ultimate newsagency. The music in my ears and the yearning it induced allowed every element of each image to be perceived as significant: a long row of grand plane trees at the edge of a series of playing fields and the partially obscured landscape beyond was in this sense just as important as the human face of Alex in the picture, which would have seemed the more obvious catalyst for my feelings. The sum total of all the surfaces in the image became the amorphous face of an ideal companion: the particular way skin, clothes, grass or dirt, absorbed and reflected light; the soft lines written into the skin by smiles and grimaces; these all told of the other, connected spaces which existed in an approximate yet obscured relation to those I was observing and turning over in my mind. I travelled through rooms with stone walls and floors where the shadows crept out of cracks, past a wooden table scattered with bottles as the sun lit up the surface of water and dark blue became a blinding white: the fleeting sounds of wind, semiconscious groans of pleasure, hands mindlessly brushing along surfaces, shaking free fragments to be lost to oblivion and collecting others that could be unfolded to reveal further strange-yet-familiar emotional worlds.

I began to type out an email to Coach Fitz. Rather than starting with the story of Alex and the events which led to me fleeing London in a state of emotional turmoil, I focused on the question of music and whether she'd support the idea of my curating a playlist for the Six Foot Track. I wondered how I could frame an argument so that she'd approve of the extra apparatus acting as a substitute for the freely imagined audience that she insisted was so valuable to the enduring desire to run, whether she might be sympathetic to the role technology could play in organically augmenting something that was already taking place, the emotional equivalent of a sailboat using the force of the wind. I wondered how I'd supplement the inevitably limited nature of the emotional renewal afforded by the songs, and whether I could build into the playlist a gradual rise up to the most intensely uplifting songs, so they were playing at the moments on the run when I needed support most.

I wrote of how I'd always been eager to fully inhabit certain songs, allowing me to interpret their content as possessing some deep truth that was irreducible to the content of the lyrics. How I let myself succumb to the particular coming together of memory, emotion and imagination that was activated by the sounds.

I wrote of how Cyndi Lauper's 'Girls Just Want to Have Fun' was among the most enduringly compelling songs in this regard and how it became the theme song to most of the thoughts I had about my three older cousins, who were all girls. Any event involving my cousins always carried with it a sense that I was being inducted into a world which until that point had been hidden from me. They were the mediators I saw as emblematising the first transitions from childhood to adulthood. Sometimes it was the injuries they inflicted during parties, such as pushing boys into creeks, dancing on tables, or telling ghost stories on the lawn about Vegemite and families being murdered by wooden dolls with long fingers. These were perhaps among my first experiences of an exclusive club to which children gained access once they had grown up.

At some point, it is hard to say exactly when, Cyndi Lauper's song so thoroughly infused my memories of this cousinly idolisation that it is now almost impossible for me to disassociate the two. Combined with imagined scenes of profound misbehaviour perpetrated by my cousins, Lauper's words carried with them what seemed an incontestable anthropological truth about teenage feminine desire. Over the years, this truth retained its persuasive purchase to a troubling degree wherever I heard the song play, vanishing as quickly as the snuffed flame of a candle when the music stopped.

I looked over to the computer next to me. The Irish girl had disappeared. The man behind the counter was absorbed in his own media-augmented world, a television comedy of some sort with lots of canned laughter. I saved the email as a draft, pressed pause on the music, and in the absence of song took one last look at the images of my travels.

Stair Sprints at Tamarama

In the days following I pondered Coach Fitz's invocation of the animal and what it might mean to reformat my body according to this image. I raised the question again with her before our next session of soft sands at Bronte Beach and the stairs in Tamarama Gully. Coach explained that the animal was an image adapted to the peculiar shape of different bodies.

To aspire to the condition of the animal has nothing to do with reverting to primal urges, she said – although, when I think about it, words like 'scuttle' and imaginings of quadrupedal action do inform my experience when I consider animality. I know it's not about being man or woman but about sensing an aliveness and the varying extent to which we are all in some respects crippled. It's maybe more a feeling in the bones than muscle. It's about how you're put together and this internal desire to transcend bodily limitations, which then oddly become the body in action.

The entire stretch of the beach was empty, apart from two girls drawing with rocks in the sand at the south end, one of whom was surprised by a wave and ended up with wet boots.

We took the stairs down to the sand at the north end and Coach, stickler that she was, turned left only at the very edge of the beach so that our first repetition encompassed its entirety. The first bit of sand leading up from the wet past the concrete stormwater drain was especially boggy. I watched Coach respond to the slope by veering sideways and tracking back as we reached level ground. The sand had migrated up the beach so that it mostly covered the exposed concrete.

The first few reps were particularly taxing with no warm-up and the recent sand run still in my legs. Coach accommodated my slowness while I continued to ply her with questions about animality. Just don't imagine smooth chests and tidy geometry, she said, imagine your capacity to move unusually, imagine the way your limbs fall, the way you hold yourself together, the energy of that togetherness in movement. She seemed to be wringing her hands of water to demonstrate this idea, flicking her wrists in a cartoonish gesture reminiscent of a petulant child.

We trudged on as the first dampening of sweat appeared on my brow and Coach began her *he-he-haas*. The ocean water was giving off a motley of different moods, with a shallow corner near the south end a tempting light blue. Further south the swell whipped into a frenzy of tight barrels, whitewash and disturbed sand, with the ominous slate-grey blues expanding further out and returning to glassy stillness in the rock-protected Bogey Hole.

At the conclusion of the tenth repetition we continued straight on up the stairs and along the coastal footpath to Tamarama Gully, which Coach told me used to be known as Wonderland City on account of the open-air amusement park that had once occupied the area.

Coach noted that the name Tamarama, which may have registered the traces of the local Aboriginal people's name for the place, Gamma Gamma, proved particularly adaptable to punning, with the media at various points favouring Dramarama and Glamarama as a way of indicating characteristics thought to be common to the more recent residents.

The beach and gully once featured attractions as varied as an ice-skating rink, a roller-coaster, an aquarium, a Japanese tearoom, a theatre, the inevitable elephant, and all manner of other novelties. When I reflect on this assortment, said Coach, it gives me great comfort that we are now able to find a more lasting kind of amusement, if that's what it must be called, in the endlessly shifting mood chambers offered underwater, or in the swells of differing magnitude that meet the shores here, or simply in the unique perspective afforded by the rock platform, its little pools of orphaned water and the impossible-to-grasp array of pinks, greens, yellows and speckled greys that fringe the edges of the channels cut into the rock.

Our Anglo ancestors were for some time poorly adapted to the affordances of the coastline, said Coach Fitz. Their expectations were determined by the miserly offerings of their grim leisure resorts, which required casinos and theme parks to brighten up the grey.

Now these, these are probably my favourite stairs in Sydney to run up, she said as we addressed the first stretch of stairs that coursed up into the bushes at the back of Tamarama Gully. They're nice and steep with a couple of gentle zigzags and subtle changes in the format of the stairs. It seems as though different parts have been restored at different times, she continued, with slightly different gradients and concrete. As far as I know they are unique. There's also the coolness provided by the stream off to the right, with some good sandstone boulders, understorey foliage and a decent tree canopy for shade in the summer months. And that's among their best features, continued Coach. Rarely do you find steps of this scale that are largely shaded. Coach stared at me for a while with the look that on our earlier meetings I thought meant she wanted a response, but had since realised was her way of driving home a point.

We completed eight repetitions in total, three from the concrete path at the bottom of the stairs and two from the drain at the bottom of the grassy gully that Coach called the 'pro's tee off', a golfing metaphor the exact meaning of which escaped me but which clearly pleased her.

I particularly appreciated the small rest we had at the top of the gully after bursting through the cool dark shade of the trees. We propped ourselves up on the white wooden railing and looked out over the houses on the north side of the gully, the road that snakes along the coast, the yellow sandstone and the ocean beyond.

Nothing like a view into the far beyond while the body is completely devoted to the task of breathing, said Coach, not to mention the bombardment of post-exercise endorphins.

On the fifth repetition an old lady in a blue swimming costume and visor joined us at a slower pace, with a small dog she was more or less dragging. How many for you? she asked delightedly. Seven, maybe eight, said Coach as we passed her. Good for you, came the reply.

On the eighth set we pushed on at the top of the stairs, all the way back to my car at Bronte. My legs were like jelly by the end, but I was buoyed by this new test and the absence of muscle aches that had accompanied some of the longer runs on hard ground.

While drying ourselves by our vehicles after the swim, Coach suggested that we ought to meet for lunch next weekend and maybe have just one glass of wine in the lobby of the Medina Hotel at Railway Square – a delightful structure, to use Coach's words, connected to one of the country's first experimental architects, Walter Liberty Vernon.

It's one of my favourite spaces to chat with athletes, said Coach. For some reason a hotel near a railway line puts me in a mood of tipsy, contemplative bliss. I think you'll find it fitting.

Lunch in the Medina

I took the train from Bondi Junction to Central and met Coach Fitz in the lobby of the Medina. A variety of saddening shops of the kind common to tourist areas and train stations made up the street-level mise-en-scène. The restaurant was on the ground floor of a massive cubic building, a former postal edifice that despite its relative age held its own amid the distractions of the area. I'd been to Central plenty of times but, as is often the case, the presence of the not-inconspicuous structure had been masked by whatever fog I had gathered around myself as I hurtled from one place to another.

Due to the generous dimensions of the room, the restaurant in the Medina was an oasis among this disagreeable mix. Coach Fitz was waiting at a table in a similar outfit to her usual, adapted slightly to the more formal context: shorts, polo shirt, and an old blue blazer that I immediately wished I owned for myself. She had already ordered a glass of white wine and was scrolling through her phone. She looked at me, smiled and we embraced.

The pasta here is quite good, said Coach as I scrutinised the menu, having my doubts. Will you have a wine? she asked, scanning the restaurant for waiters in a jittery fashion.

Having wine at lunch was a transgression I had allowed myself on very few occasions. The idea delighted me when I witnessed couples indulging in such behaviour, but confronted with the prospect of being inducted into that community by a figure who still seemed largely anomalous, I regarded the invitation with a disproportionate amount of dread.

I'm having the chardonnay, said Coach, perhaps sensing my vulnerability at this point of indecision.

Next time the waiter came around I went through the routine of ordering my wine, though stripped of the excitement I'd thought I would feel when imagining such an occasion. I had no stake in the idea now, and whether this was true or not, felt it foisted upon me by the tacit presumptions of Coach Fitz, who sat there enjoying her wine in a divinely untroubled fashion.

Still with her head inclined towards her phone, and prodding the device occasionally as though it were an unfamiliar pet, Coach began a discourse on the style of the building. The Parcels Post Office, she began, naming the building that now housed the Medina, conforms to a type I find reliably pleasing. It is a large brick building, the most striking feature of which is its confident squareness. Maybe it's hard to justify devotion to an object due to this attribute alone, but I comfort myself in the notion that attitudes of endearment are often characterised by extreme specificity, the most commonly acknowledged terms we use for these being fetishes and phobias.

So you have a fetish for squareness? I asked.

If we strip from that word any connotations to do with the sexual, and return it to something closer to its original usage, which denoted an object worshipped for magical powers, then yes, I have a fetish for certain varieties of squareness and the sense of unbudgeability they tend to evoke.

We both ordered the same pasta, a fusilli with cheeses, mushroom, roast cauliflower, pine nuts, raisins and truffle oil.

During the ordering process I noticed Coach's poor manner with the waiters. It wasn't rudeness, but rather a seeming inability to allow the dialogue to unfold harmoniously. I would have assumed she was deaf if I didn't know she could hear perfectly well in other contexts. It was as though Coach were deliberately muddying the airwaves so the waiter left our table feeling bemused and perhaps insulted. When Coach ordered the pasta and the waiter repeated the order, she needlessly corrected him even though he'd got the order right. No, we said the *fusilli*, spelling the word out as if the waiter were a child. She expressed this with such a pronounced degree of frustration that I couldn't help but inherit some of the bad feelings I imagined the waiter to be enduring.

After this ordeal, Coach stopped and looked up with a playful, disbelieving grin and continued her dialogue about squareness and her penchant for the architecture of Vernon, to whose buildings she attributed a simultaneous sense of the solid and the light. Juggling these contrasting moods, said Coach, is the mark of much great architecture.

When the pasta arrived Coach ordered another wine, and while I was only halfway through mine she ordered another for me too. I began bracing myself for a lost afternoon, the upshot of which might have been a greater tolerance, and a lessening in the mild irritation and uncertainty, that at that moment characterised my feelings toward Coach Fitz.

The pasta was very average, a great recipe that in execution somehow lacked nuance, overcooked, too much oil, bad cheese. Yet Coach said it was among the finest things she'd ever tasted and continually remarked on its features, in particular the occasional swollen raisin hidden within the cheesy sauce, which she would pick out with her fingers, hold up to her eyes and say, this is the *raison d'être*!

The wine however was an excellent match for the food and in the haze of my sudden drunkenness I soon began to forget my negative emotions. Coach continued to wax lyrical about the inaccuracies of the category 'Federation style', about the regrettable pervasiveness of rectangularity as opposed to squareness in the CBD, and about the Parcels Post Office's previous history as a place of refuge for women who had fallen into hardship in the mid-to-late nineteenth century.

When the waiter came to collect our plates I pointedly resisted Coach's efforts to order me another wine. I could see that she was disappointed by the prospect of having to go it alone for the last round. But go it alone she did, and without the promise of my inhibitions undergoing a further loosening, I felt a growing keenness for the occasion to wind up, so I could rescue the afternoon from a fate of mild dehydration and fuzzy-headedness.

This final wine sustained Coach through a discourse on a way of framing endurance training that she believed to be peculiar to her practice. You must think of yourself as training your training, Coach declared, as tautological as that might sound. Once you have accumulated enough kilometres in your legs you will be accompanied by a background of training that you need to direct according to a rhythmic harmony of contrasting training sessions, with many variations in intensity and tempo. I could tell Coach was on a roll. Her voice became louder and her advice harder to comprehend. You're training your training, she continued, and without this *epoque de longue durée* approach to a running program, efforts to peak during race time tend to lack the substance they otherwise might possess.

As Coach became tipsy the whistle in her speech became more pronounced and more than once she spat involuntarily while she spoke. The background is where it all begins, she said. It is here also where you must establish an approach to running that is at once purposeful and carefree, ensuring you allow your body to adapt gradually to the rigours of long-distance training. Think of yourself as a boxer devoting the first stages of their training to footwork alone, resisting the temptation to satisfy your building urges to burst forth and thus exhaust yourself prematurely. Run long, run often, and run without pressure, that way your body settles into the required rhythm that is the necessary foundation from which your more intense periods of training might explode.

Though Coach's discourse was enlightening, I couldn't rid myself of the thought that if she ordered another wine we might be there until late afternoon. I said that I had to visit my auntie in Beecroft to help her shift a lounge, and needed to get an early night's sleep so I didn't start the work week on the back foot. Of this Coach was surprisingly understanding and, after gesturing to the waiter in a way that I could only imagine he'd interpret as a signal of distress, she generously offered to pay for my meal.

After settling the bill we both stood for a while at the foot of the former parcels office, its cubic form bulging proudly above the visual and sonic noise that pervaded the street level.

The massing makes the ornament appear right, said Coach, like the military uniforms that have often been a source of inspiration for designers. At this she brought my body near with her arms and embraced me tightly. I felt the soft, worn fabric of her blazer against my face and hands and when she released me I saw that Coach might have had a tear in her eye.

I walked off waving without turning back and imagined that she might have stood there for some time yet, admiring the sturdy island of brick as the flows of people in and out of the station parted to accommodate her. I passed through the Devonshire Street tunnel back to Central Station, wondering about Coach's sex life. She had not mentioned prior partners and had something of the eternal spinster about her, yet there was undoubtedly a muscular eroticism to the way she expressed herself and admired other bodies. Inevitably I pondered where I was positioned in this hypothetical field of desire. Did she want to strip me of my clothes and grind her body up and down mine? Did an appetite inform her encouragements? Did she imagine us together in crisp lemon-smelling sheets? Would we fornicate on the porch like two chaotic strips of rubber? Would she float down to me and take both my cheeks in her small hands? Would she inspect my scrotum and my penis? Or did she imagine herself as my mother, the host of my emotions? A genius that would prod and cajole me with immunising mixtures of inspiration and criticism? The wine had been reactivated by the music of the buskers in the tunnel and instead of catching the train back to Edgecliff I decided to run off my excesses, and sprinted up the stairs at the eastern end and out into the day.

Coach's Failings

After these early training sessions and dialogues with Coach Fitz, my impeccable conception of her began to accumulate some enduring niggles. The first fault I identified was a tendency to discuss her ailments at length. Coach would often begin a discussion by meticulously describing a vague but evidently defining psychophysical disturbance. It was like the illness was the substitute for the dog or the child of a new and besotted owner or mother.

On one such occasion she speculated that some bug, as she called it, was having a subtle, transformative effect on a series of activities Coach thought of as key to her sense of vitality. She said that the sickness would seem to retreat after some moderate exercise, only to return again when she spent any length of time in certain interior environments, particularly anything air-conditioned or lit with fluorescent lighting. The illness was detectable as a mild pain behind her eyes and what she described as an electric, metallic taste in her mouth, coupled with an increased abundance of hot, watery saliva. Coach asked me whether I ever used the sense of pressure behind my eyes as an indicator of my wellbeing, to which I replied in the negative.

If this were the exception rather than the norm it wouldn't have seemed peculiar. However, the regularity with which Coach spoke of her ailments made it seem as though her very being could be expressed only as some kind of vague pathology waiting to be given a more stable classification by the medical community.

Her speculations often revolved around the question of what foods seemed most appropriate to return her immune system to equilibrium, or whether exercise would fuel or inhibit a malaise. She couldn't resist the temptation to bring these departures from the norm more fully into being by elaborating their various characteristics and spreading them as rumours via text messages to her friends and disciples.

It feels as though there is another face inside my face trying to get out, she would say, or, I feel awful until I close my eyes for five or so minutes and then I am immediately restored, only for my condition to gradually deteriorate again, until I re-enter darkness and quiet.

Coach, of course, was fully aware of this tendency and put it down to what she described as her elite intropathic abilities, coupled with the expectation that she should possess a complete knowledge of her bodily functioning.

I also noticed Coach Fitz would longingly look into some of the pubs we passed on our runs, especially those with tiles on the outside and minimal branding on the exterior awnings. On one morning in particular she looked as though she was carrying the signs of an alcohol-fuelled evening, with a distinctive red mark appearing on the bridge of her nose and a sour smell that I knew well as the scent of a grog-lover.

I had no way of comfortably addressing her in a direct fashion on the matter, so I spoke of my own love of pubs in the hope that she might reveal something of her habit. There's nothing quite like the promise offered by a pub, is there, I would say, to which Coach would reply in profound agreement and stare away at some distant unmanifest thing, leaving it at that.

Coach Fitz also began to spend a lot of time using her smartphone. She had upgraded about a year before to a new device and was now increasingly engrossed by the perpetual access to knowledge and communication it granted. Often when we'd meet, instead of stretching, I would find her with a bent neck and finger hovering, making regular stabbing motions at the screen. She might then integrate the phone in some bizarre manner into the stretch itself, wedging it between a clutched knee and her torso, or placing it between her face and the ground while she flexed into any of a number of downward poses.

On these occasions I couldn't help but imagine Coach's form as a statue that some future population might look upon to register the defining aspects of our epoch. Coach would often attempt to read and even write messages on our run, making me feel as though I was practised in a monkish ability to ignore my own device.

Occasionally I found myself overcome by a sense of disappointment, even disgust, not so much at Coach Fitz but at my earlier naïve imaginings of her perfection. Observing such behaviour I had the inkling that Coach's philosophy was not as coherent as I once thought, and that she often didn't follow her own advice. Despite recognising that I was viewing her through the prism of my high expectations, I felt disillusioned. How quickly the inspiration of our initial romance can transform or expire, I thought to myself, and eventually each master reveals the hidden aspect in which they too are a novice in need of training, unable to obtain a perspective on their own faults. How does a coach negotiate the inevitable expression of their own vulnerabilities without putting their authority at risk?

I pondered these questions as I sat alone on the rock platform at Mackenzies Bay some time later, tearing strips off a sourdough loaf and dousing them in generous glugs of olive oil. The air was thick with salt and moisture and though I'd readied myself for a cloudy humid day, the sun was now beginning to make an appearance.

These were the perfect conditions for swimming in the rock channel, I thought to myself, and after making some solid inroads into my loaf, I picked a tentative trail across the barnacles, pink lichens and the translucent green dags of seaweed strewn across the rocks. I thought back to those days with Coach Fitz and tried to weigh up whether the key lessons she'd taught me were the ones she'd intended to convey, or whether I'd gleaned the more profound insights from lessons she would have never imagined herself to impart.

_____

Helensburgh to Bundeena

Sensing I was ready for a significant challenge, Coach suggested a run from Otford to Bundeena, through Royal National Park just south of Sydney. We were to meet at Redfern Station at 9.30 a.m. and take the train to Otford where we would begin our run.

It was an uncharacteristically summery morning for a late winter month. Coach noted that it seemed as though Sydney had decided to skip spring altogether, and mentioned that a day in the car yesterday had left her with some kind of bowel disturbance, the symptoms of which included nausea, peculiar stools and bloating.

We stood for a while outside the ticket office to Redfern Station, Coach pointing out the building as a fine example of the Queen Anne style and noting her appreciation of the unusual bluish colour of the turret against the terracotta. What a sight, she said, and as you'll see inside the ceiling isn't bad to look at either.

We waited underground on Platform 12, which was pervaded by a smell of dirt circulated by strange breezes. The train was tightly packed when we boarded and Coach and I did our best to read the Saturday papers, my eyes on the racing form while she tacked between reading an article on sleep science for elite athletes and working out the quickest route to Otford on her phone.

After discussing the trajectory of the train and its stoppages with a number of passengers, Coach decided that it would be in our best interests to begin our run in Helensburgh rather than Otford, saving us from waiting on the platform for a connecting train. She claimed she knew the route from the station to the beginning of the Burgh Track that we would follow until it met with the Coast Track near the delightfully named Burning Palms Beach.

Coach navigated with ease through the backstreets leading up to the trail, but began to falter as we moved from the tarmac to a fire trail. A pair of dog walkers showed puzzlement that we would consider running such a distance, but didn't offer much help.

We cut a tentative course through what looked to be a mixture of bushland and rubbish tip, with partially burnt car seats, exhaust piping strung up in branches and pink flannel pyjama pants nailed to the trunk of a tree. Aside from the intermittent gusts of wind and the occasional birdcall, it was utterly still and silent, the bush an almost overwhelming enclosure of detail, a peculiarly adapted force of growth and decay. We followed the trail down the hill until we met with the railway track as it emerged from a nearby tunnel, looking quite incongruous in such a setting. With no obvious route to the other side of the track we decided to retrace our steps to the end of the tarmac and work out our way from there.

On the way back we crossed paths with two blokes in a dual-cab ute taking their three dogs for a ride in the back. Grasping what Coach was on about, despite her confusion, they gave us a lift in the tray to a gate in the fence, which they unlocked before pointing us up a promising-looking trail, and leaving with the advice that we keep our eyes on the left side of the track to spot a national park sign that was easy to miss. Both men were adorned in sprays of tattoos and the more talkative of the two had taken to calling me cobber from a swollen mouth, 'Good luck, cobber', while seeming to ignore Coach.

I imagined them stalking down the track and setting their dogs loose on us, so the first part of the run was completed in good time. We sped downhill along a fire trail and managed to spot the small sign that pointed into the classic east-coast dry sclerophyll, with its terracotta-trunked angophoras, stout palms, stringybarks, piles of leaf litter and bulges of spinifex-like grass.

We then descended into wet sclerophyll, followed by a rainforest track along the Hacking River. The recent discovery of Coach's alcoholic odour and facial redness was on my mind, so I began a line of questioning I hoped would elicit some truth as to her obscure motivations and behaviour.

Remember what you told me about Charlie Samuels? I asked, to which Coach huffed in agreement. Well, I too find myself tempted by the bottle sometimes. Do you ever face such challenges?

Coach made it clear that she wasn't going to give me anything but obfuscation and, true to her way, turned the discussion to my own sexual history with a question about my attitude to sex and whether I perceived myself to have any control over the things I desired when it came to such matters.

It was plain that Coach saw our relationship as contingent on her being in the position of therapist, with myself as patient, and I began to wonder if it was my willingness to adopt this role that endeared me to Coach in the first place.

Uncomfortable with the idea of fighting to get some truth out of her about her relationship with alcohol, I played along, telling Coach I viewed my expectations and desires as a mess of inherited ideas and failures. Clearly this was the answer she'd hoped for, and so began a lengthy but insightful discourse on male entitlement, and how clumsily and unimaginatively our society deals with the issue of sex, her disquisition broken only by the extra effort required on the steeper terrain after Lady Wakehurst Parkway and the technical descent down to Era Beach after the car park at Garrawarra Farm.

We think of ourselves as enlightened on the issue, said Coach, as though our sex-splashed media were an indicator we have a good grasp of the subject. We are fascinated by a certain form of sexualised representation but there is little in the entertainment system that educates with regard to the complexity, fluidity and diversity of what each sex, and indeed each individual, expects from and feels in the act.

The young men who live on a diet of intermittent, opportunistic sex during their years of adolescence form warped ideas about what pleases other people in bed, she continued. Their maladapted sex practices are not the product of evil but laziness. The absence of information from inspirational sources allows the influence of grim, sadomasochistic video performances we give the misleadingly innocuous name porn.

We trudged through the sand on Era Beach, catching occasional wafts of dead things and wattles, before leaping a little lagoon and beginning a steep climb up the next headland. Little shacks coupled with freshwater tanks dotted the landscape, and the often bald, grassy headlands and wide views up the coastland over the ocean offered an intense contrast to the enclosed feeling of the forest, with its abundance of timber, tree litter and vegetation of varying scales.

Coach continued with her teachings, offering impassioned remarks about how immense care and exceptional communication were the only means to create sexual outcomes beneficial to both parties. She spoke of how the sex act ought to be an opportunity for cycles of mutual debasement and loss of identity, saying that it takes a sustained and guided effort to recognise that the relationship between teleology – which I took to be her word for sexual climax – and pleasure differed greatly between individuals.

I reflected on my own experience and admitted to Coach that for me sex and its completion were so tightly intertwined that it was difficult to imagine the event without it being entirely coloured by the idea of a climax. I resisted the temptation at this point to engineer a digression in which I would be able to reveal the more specific troubles in my romantic life and my time overseas with Alex – particularly as Coach seemed content with my confessions so far, nodding vigorously and suggesting that the same climax-oriented attitude is what drives most runners. The idea of completing something, the idea of a finish, Coach continued, it requires an active effort to train this not altogether pernicious mentality so it works alongside other drives relating to continuity, spontaneity and expression.

With regard to running, Coach offered, one of my approaches is to target the warm-up and cool-down as key sites to promote optimal performance. At a certain stage in my training program I ask runners to reflect on how their warm-up and cool-down functions in their running practice. Most use it as an arbitrary ten- or twenty-minute addition to the beginning or end of the usual running session. I make the simple suggestion of reducing the length of their running session by ten minutes and adding five minutes onto the warm-up and cool-down. I encourage them to think about the possibility that the warm-up and cool-down is the most important part of the run, that it *sets the tone*. Then we have a bit of fun and do runs that consist of ninety per cent warm-up, or runs consisting entirely of three warm-ups. We sometimes elongate the warm-up gradually so that runs might go as much as three or four times as long as the usual session.

My aim is to normalise a warm-up of substance and to promote thought about the possibilities of the run/warm-up format, said Coach. It shouldn't take a particularly subtle intellect to work out the correspondence between this approach to running and what goes on in the bedroom.

It was at this point in the run that I noticed, whenever Coach turned back to check for my agreement, a moustache of sweat had formed across her top lip, and that she was giving off a smell of fermented passionfruit. From the top of the next headland I could see down to Garie Beach and the sizable headland beyond. The air was manifest as a light haze that added to the sense of adventure.

We followed the footpath down to the rocky edge of the beach and stopped to buy refreshments at the small tuckshop, Coach a cola and me a lemon-lime sports drink.

My memory of the next stretch of the run is blurred by fatigue. It was the longest and most demanding run that I'd been on yet, made more difficult by Coach suggesting repetitions of some of the harder stretches along sand or uphill. We passed through gauntlets of stunted casuarinas and freshened ourselves in cool, clear streams of water that emerged from the bush and toppled over headlands into the ocean. Coach took the approach of dipping her hat in the water and replacing it on her head, a process she described as 'wetting the rat'. We ran across sandstone bluffs pockmarked by pools of water, through the car park at Wattamolla, and past the nearby lagoon, before returning to the sandstone cliffs from which we could see the track ahead of us stretching north to Bundeena, marked out along the cape.

The bar of chocolate Coach had saved especially for this taxing stretch had completely melted and we had to more or less drink it out of its foil wrapper in turns. Instead of providing the respite I'd hoped for, it merely served to gum up my mouth. Before long Coach had the stuff all over her hands and face.

At times the rubble-strewn terrain looked like moonscape, and one particular section of rock was so white and perfectly formed it induced a desire to cut into it like a wedding cake.

We completed a few desperate trudges across steeply sloping sand beaches, managing to dodge the swell while running on the harder wet ground before dragging ourselves up a last couple of headlands and following the root-strewn trail through the shrubbery to the tarmac on the outskirts of Bundeena, a sight that brought great relief.

We stretched at length on a patch of grass by a small creek that ran out into the beach. I found myself in the difficult situation of needing to stretch to relieve cramp, but not being able to stretch due to the cramping I was experiencing. I felt a stiffness and pain deep in my muscles that mixed with a sense of satisfaction fractionally though distinctively different from what I'd felt on shorter runs.

When we had coffee afterwards it seemed my metabolism had been renewed to its early-adolescent status, where caffeine had a pronounced, near-ecstatic effect that continued at a slow ebb for the rest of the day.

Coach stocked up on yet more newspapers for the return journey to Cronulla Station that went via the small ferry. I looked at her immersed in the great, continually shifting mess of chocolate-smudged sheets strewn across her lap, and asked whether she ever got sick of being updated with information that seemed not to be of any real importance.

At this Coach folded the paper and looked sideways and up. The newspaper is the modern human's prayer, she offered. Realising this wasn't an adequate response, and perhaps feeling the pinch of not having responded directly to any of my earlier enquiries, she continued: At some point in my life the news I received in the paper began to seem to me as though it was news sent from some authority, something of which I ought to take notice. It came to signify both leisure and a particular form of access, a comfort blanket of sorts, a surrogate or umbilical link that sustained me by offering a support system of interest.

As often seemed to be the case, Coach's insight gave conceptual form to a habit of my own that had previously remained obscure, and I shared what until then had been a dirty secret.

Since my grandfather's death I had returned to my old routine of buying the *Best Bets* racing form, ideally on a Thursday afternoon when the information was hot off the press, and placing a few modest bets on the Saturday races, usually from the dark, cool, largely empty environment of a pub such as the Glengarry on Abercrombie Street in Darlington.

This was in part the continuation of a tradition that I'd begun during my adolescence, a period I often described to Coach as characterised by feelings of impotence. The idea that I might pick a winner replaced what I saw as the twofold limitations placed on my existence by the restrictive environment of boarding school and my relatively diminutive physique.

I had during my primary school years and into early high school been a member of the athletics team, but before long my contemporaries began to transform into hulking, hairy things against whom it was hopeless for me to try and compete until some reserves of testosterone arrived. The horseraces provided me, as I presumed it did for my grandfather after the premature end to his athletics career, an opportunity to gain some form of acquaintance with a new sense of potential, not as someone who could outrun their competitors but as someone who had the gift of divining the meaning that was coded into the otherwise meaningless or near-meaningless information in the form guide. The winners were there for me to see if I immersed myself in the information in a sustained fashion and with the right attitude.

After getting a taste for the atmosphere of the track while attending a few meets at Rosehill Race Course with my grandad and his friends, men with names like Lesley, Desmond and Noel, I would make the journey out to Warwick Farm in a pair of tracksuit pants, clutching the *Best Bets* while my friends emptied their energies into the upkeep of the school spirit by supporting the various sporting teams that competed on the weekend. Each time I had to rely on the bookies' responding to my clearly underage efforts in good humour. The craze only petered out when I discovered that I could augment my physique through developing a training regime in the gym, and in this way combat my perceived impotence in the esteem of my female contemporaries, who were fast becoming the sole arbiters of worth in my mind.

Like all addictive rituals, my punting involved a highly specific set of continually evolving requirements. The form guide had to be the *Best Bets*. There was something right about the pocket-sized format and the layout that featured colourful jockeys' silks next to each runner. I also enjoyed the lively, often humorous style of its editors, I continued. It was a deep disappointment whenever I was forced to make do with the admittedly more detailed the *Sportsman* or even, god forbid, the *Wizard*.

The newsagencies from which I purchased the *Best Bets* also took on the air of something important. They were my providers, giving me access to the format that enabled the pleasure of my predictions. A feeling of things being in order always overcame me when I saw the small, colourful package of the *Best Bets* displayed behind the perspex shelf in front of the other dull and flabby racing papers.

During my spare time in the Odyssey in between jobs, I would splay the *Best Bets* open on my lap and allow myself the luxury of assessing some of the tipsters' predictions at length.

I shared all this in a more halting fashion with Coach as we travelled back to Redfern on the Eastern Suburbs and Illawarra Line. At various points in my discourse Coach would get up in the aisle and encourage me to follow her in a series of stretches focused on the glutes, hip flexors, quads, calves and lower back, all of which were becoming increasingly sore.

On this occasion more than any other I saw that Coach received my confessions with a sense of warmth, avidly nodding throughout and encouraging me with yeses and low hums of agreement.

When I finished she reassured me that the perceiving of special information in periodicals wasn't an uncommon practice. For instance, said Coach, one of my previous students would meticulously circle the specials on offer in various shopping catalogues, although he never purchased any of the products – and my mother and her friends would organise weekly gatherings to discuss the discoveries in the catalogues that arrived in their various letter boxes.

Coach suggested that I might try finding a surrogate for the *Best Bets* by replacing it with another periodical that did not share the same connection to the gambling and horseracing industries, which despite their central place in the history I shared with my grandfather, ought to be regarded not as a benevolent force, but as one connected to pernicious habits.

You need to update your solitude techniques, she said, and enquired as to whether I was able to call to mind any fields of interest less well established in my routines that nonetheless delivered a comparable sense of excitement.

The thing you need to find, said Coach, is a publication that you might receive semi-regularly, something that involves experts and the dramatisation of their discriminatory faculties. Ideally something related to where you live.

After we parted near the station I mused at length on Coach's question, making vague arrangements for a run again soon, next weekend at the latest.

As I made my way back to the Odyssey, down Redfern Street past the sets of terrace houses and melaleucas, I passed the Glengarry, a pleasingly wedge-shaped pub on the corner, and decided to drop in for a beer and see if there were perhaps any interesting prospects in the day's final races.

While sipping my beer, and attempting to make predictions based on the inadequate racing information displayed in the weekend *Herald*, I realised that for some time I had been incubating in my mind the perfect candidate to replace punting and the hints of trouble I was coming to associate with the habit.

Since my later high school days I enjoyed reading the café and restaurant reviews and other food-related suggestions in what was then called the Good Living section of the *Sydney Morning Herald*. I regarded the advice outlined in the pages of the Tuesday supplement to be of a special kind, a fact often puzzled at by my friends who then gave me the label 'rustic bourgeoisie' on account of the pretensions associated with the publication and with food criticism in general. None of this mattered to me because I was on the *inside*, so to speak, a believer in the good news featured in the pages.

In a very real sense, the Good Living was gospel. Whatever the items regarding new restaurants, bakeries, providores and bottles of wine and beer suggested, they were meaningful to me in a comparable way to the selections and display of information on show in the *Best Bets*. In contrast to my relationship to the *Best Bets*, I was under less of an interpretive burden with Good Living, with the main requirement consisting not in weighing up alternative candidates on which to bet, but rather in forming an idea in my head of where the goods and services under consideration could be viewed, bought and experienced, and how the event of my collecting or encountering them might be woven into my weekly routines.

In the absence of an actual visit, I was simply happy to inhabit a restaurant, café or bar virtually, which, considering my means, was what I did almost exclusively during the years of my apprenticeship to the Good Living at high school.

I wondered whether my strong feelings for this information were a consequence of the role the publication played in my school days, when I spent a good deal of time imagining the freedoms of early adulthood, key among them buying dinner out in restaurants and drinking alcohol in pubs and bars. I read about wasabi mash, tapas, Balmain bugs, scallops, bruschetta and duck confit. I imagined people drinking cocktails in the street in jaunty but unadventurous outfits, smiling with the knowledge that an evening of diverse and steadily intensifying pleasures awaited. It was as though those imaginings from the last days of the previous millennium had crystallised within me and continued to offer a source of motivation, impervious to the ridicule of my contemporaries.

I looked up from the paper to the screen, to some anonymous race in Western Australia, where the daylight still extended and where the dry bush which overlooked the course appeared an unlikely thing to be captured in the media and then find its way into this pub on the other side of the country.

I thought back to my early days with the Good Living in the first years of the new millennium, when the chief critic was Matthew Evans, and how I had developed an increasingly involved fantasy dialogue with the section's subsequent critics, Simon Thomsen and Terry Durack.

As per Coach's suggestions, I reflected on the minutiae of the practices that were so pervasive in my life that their importance seemed self-evident and therefore difficult to articulate. I began to recognise a distinctive set of routines I'd built around reading the Good Living which until that point had remained inexplicit.

The first thing that came to mind was the game I played with reading the review section, where the critic offered a written evaluation of a restaurant and score out of twenty. After buying the paper on Tuesday I would conduct what was essentially a flirting ritual with the review, circling it like a shark on my initial reconnaissance reads of the paper and often managing to last until Thursday when I would, at the end of the day, ideally during a meal time, finally confront the review, marking the event rhetorically by vocalising expressions such as *What have you got for me now, Durack*, and *Ah, Durack, we meet again*, and sometimes, at the review's conclusion, *Durack, you're such a dick*.

For some unknown reason my dialogue with the current reviewer had taken on a tone of theatricalised antagonism, as though in reading the review I was in something of an ongoing duel with the writer. I suspected that this attitude was in part provoked, very unfairly, by Durack's floppy hair and an image I'd hallucinated where he was wearing what appeared to be a lavender-coloured suit.

Another section of the Good Living that brought purpose to my life was the page of wine reviews by Huon Hooke. I found this section particularly important due to its naming of the different bottle shops that were named as housing the wines under review. In more recent times this gave me the opportunity to take the Odyssey to some place I might otherwise not visit and enabled me to build up an ever-improving mental catalogue of my favourite bottle shops, including Kemenys on Bondi Road, Vine Providore in Redfern, Platinum Liquor in Bellevue Hill, Prince Wine Store in Zetland and Summer Hill Wine Shop. Once sourced, I would stow the wine under the seat of the car and reflect regularly on its being there during moments of boredom or unease experienced throughout the day.

Pleased with these discoveries, I finished my beer without placing any bets, and wandered down the dark streets to seek out a rewarding meal for the evening.

Botany Road

Coach had told me to be at the ready for a run down Botany Road as soon as the weather got a bit hotter. She said that she had to answer a deep need to immerse herself in the wattle smells of early spring while tracing that particular route from Redfern Station all the way down to the port near the Sir Joseph Banks Park where I'd run my laps in the months prior.

It just seems like a good place to be on a hot day, she said, something about the combination of industry from the different eras, the glimpses you catch of old weatherboard houses and humble churches, some of which, she reassured me with a nod, make you feel as though you're in the south-west of America. Coach emphasised that we would lather ourselves up with sunscreen and get ice creams to ensure the full atmospheric effect of summer.

The hot day arrived and with it a northerly wind that was at our backs for the first stretch. We sailed along the footpath past the remnants of brick factories converted into apartments, self-storage facilities and car dealerships. This, said Coach Fitz, is the postmodern city, the heritage-listed brick shells of industry giving birth to minimalist apartment blocks distinguishing themselves in a contradiction of gaudy minor flourishes: feature walls, anodyne sculptures made from leftover materials, fake structural elements added to give the appearances of a functionalist modern style.

Certain strips were populated by kebab shops, fish-and-chipperies, Thai restaurants, bottle-os, cafés and pubs, while others featured garages, apartments and the old weatherboard houses that Coach often stopped to admire. She drew my attention to two red-brick Art Deco façades: the red-and-yellow paint scheme of one followed the contours of the brickwork, making it look like a giant, dormant, Transformer robot. Coach remarked on the peculiar compulsion to ruin good buildings with paint, in the name of reducing maintenance or signalling deals.

The other façade was preserved without paintwork. Coach thought it an instructive comparison, illustrating how nice the first building might look if left unslathered. I was unsure of my own feelings about the paint and even thought that more elaborate decoration might improve the thing. Coach became particularly animated at the sight of some two-storey red-brick apartments with curved corners, and a light-pink cottage with a green, steeply sloping corrugated iron roof and two white columns. We passed several churches on the first stretch that seemed particularly surprising in a context dominated by industry and modern transport, with aeroplanes passing overhead, circling overpasses and traffic streaming past.

These churches, in particular one of weatherboard and another surrounded by solid palm trees, along with the swampy wetlands we soon came to, did indeed give the place the feel of a naïvely imagined American South-west, a fact which I remarked upon to Coach who said the distinctive, heady atmosphere of the area made her feel as though she was entering a place of profound mystery whenever she ran down here.

We ran through a gauntlet of branches thick with sweet, musky wattle smells, and passed a decent stand of swamp oaks before Coach paused to read the information panel at the Botany Wetlands, which described the area as the largest freshwater wetland in Sydney. Ringed by overpasses, corporate parks and golf courses, it was pleasing to stare for a while into the thick, muddy morass of lilies and other underwater plants, and for a moment to feel as though we were staring into some churning portal that led back to the primordial soup. Coach noted that the swamps and sandy soil, along with banksia scrub, would have once been the dominant geological and botanical features of the region now known as the Botany Lowlands.

Remember the sandy soil we trod through around the perimeter of Centennial Park? Coach asked. That's part of the same geological community. It gives me great comfort to think, she continued, that there is a large volume of water resting or flowing in the sandy ground beneath me whenever I run over this terrain.

Coach reaffirmed this observation before we set off again, noting that there was something in general about the notion of underground water that seemed to supply her with a sense of imaginative belonging and calm, and that I too should work to establish geological or domestic atmospheres which would reliably induce such agreeable affects.

The wind picked up and I worried about the abundance of plane tree fibres I'd noted earlier in the day. Coach suggested we quicken our pace for the next three kilometres before we stopped for refreshments. She began to offer a theory on why the Botany area appealed to her but, realising we should focus on running, abruptly cut the discourse off before starting up again as we refilled our bottles at one of the many 'secret taps' she had located to ensure a reliable source of water on her running tracks. I was surprised that the barely visible thing protruding from a beaten-up brick wall managed a stream of water, and puzzled at the idea of how she'd found it, but soon enough our bottles were brimming, the water bearing only the faintest tinge of rust brown.

What it is about Botany, Coach continued, is that it seems an exemplary case of the architectural messiness that defines Sydney more broadly. Everything is a wandering motley of styles, often bearing little or no relationship to the surrounding buildings or landscape.

Coach demonstrated this with particular glee shortly afterwards when pointing out Botany Fire Station on Banksia Street. This is a fine example of the Federation Arts and Crafts style, she said, but it is a lonesome vestige among houses that each, to varying degrees of force and vivacity, express a style peculiar to themselves. In Botany we witness a rich and varied display of the past one hundred years, with domestic, industrial, religious and recreational artefacts squashed in alongside each other. None of it quite evokes the melancholy of a ruin, but, to the outsider at least, there's a lack of overt contrivance that I hope, perhaps naïvely, ought to characterise the built environment.

We continued on Banksia Street before taking the perimeter track around the ample fields of Booralee Park, with Coach remarking that it was the Indigenous way of saying Botany. Unfortunately we didn't manage to find the old horse trough, which Coach assured me she had seen before, uncovered in the park during an archaeological dig, but we did find an old toilet block beneath a sizeable Moreton Bay fig, and a large group of ibis perched at intervals on the fronds of the palms surrounding a war memorial, at which point we both agreed that a large palm tree would be a good spot for a bird to perch and take stock for a while.

The park was gazetted in the 1920s, said Coach, which roughly marks the time when the old fishing village of Booralee began to enter into the symbolic realm. The new focus on international trade and transport involved dramatic alterations to the landscape that irrevocably changed the liminal underwater environment where fish and other sea creatures had previously been abundant.

We watched the assembled ibis unfold and inspect their wings. Of course new animals will come to thrive in the environments we create, I offered, which Coach responded to with a frown. Yes, she said, I suppose we'll need to start eating ibis.

We met up with the main drag again and took the less salubrious route along O'Riordan back towards Redfern, fighting a nasty headwind and floating shrapnel from the plane trees. Before parting we ducked into a mixed business that Coach noted was one of her favourites. It featured ample aisles of newspapers and magazines and had the slightly sour smell I had observed to emit from the deep creases of some books.

Coach and I browsed the different sections for a while, occasionally lifting and flicking through a magazine to see the messages it was attempting to transmit. The atmosphere reminded me of the internet café I favoured on Bondi Road, and I began to wonder whether now might be the time to either bring up some of the questions I'd been forming about certain seemingly irresolvable contradictions in Coach's views on the value of entertainment and media augmentation, or lay the foundations for a future meeting where, in a more relaxed atmosphere, I could open up about my failures overseas and my relationship with Alex. The difficulty with the second option was the likelihood of having to once again endure Coach under the influence of booze.

Coach tapped me on the shoulder, handed me a Calippo icy pole and gestured towards the exit. We re-entered the hot wind of the day, bid each other farewell and walked in opposite directions. Some way down the road, I turned and yelled back. Coach! She swung around on the spot as though eternally ready for the suggestion. How about another lunch? Sure. Sure. I know just the spot. I'll shoot you an email. And she swung around again with a wave, leaving me to once again ponder my feelings about the lopsided distribution of agency that informed our decisions about places of recreation.

Trumper Park

The following week, on a perfect, sunny afternoon, Coach and I met at Trumper Park in Woollahra. The plan was to complete a speed session on the oval and then head to a pub up the road for a meal and a beer. I parked my car on the lower stretches of Glenmore Road and wandered down the hill to find Coach admiring the original sandstone gates that date the park to the early twentieth century. There was something charmingly redundant in such a conspicuous set of gates orphaned from any fence work. We admired the large, smooth-barked eucalypts clustered to the side of the gate and took the opportunity to experience crossing the grand threshold, walking through the gate and following the tarmac path to the picket fence of the oval.

The oval was looking a picture. After suggesting that the day had been carefully conceived in the mind of a benevolent being and offered to us as a reward for our commitment, Coach revealed that the session would be six four-hundred-metre repetitions, followed by five kilometres at a pace that I could imagine myself running for a marathon.

Like many of the great ovals we visited, Trumper Park was nestled at the base of a sloping hillside, giving it the effect of a natural amphitheatre and the sense of drama Coach thought desirable in training venues. Among the city parks, Trumper Park stood out because this sloping area was in good part made from bushland, with large trees and thick understorey comprising roughly half of the oval's eastern side.

Above the bushland, the flags atop the Edgecliff Centre flapped lightly in the breeze and for a while I pondered the ecology peculiar to that building's interior: a clientele of a distinctively elderly and well-moneyed variety, the wood panelling and old diner that recalled the shopping centres of rural NSW, the crinkle-cut chips from the takeaway shop that I occasionally favoured on my lunch breaks between window-washing and after-school care, the sample portions of sausage sizzling in the electric pan out the front of the butcher, the cubes of ciabatta and olive oil at the front of the deli.

The oval was marked out in black lines for a school athletics carnival and these spurred me on as I rounded the bends of my 400s in the exuberant and joyful fashion I hoped would characterise all my displays of physical effort. Coach completed a few herself alongside me, while the rest of the time she egged me on with her favourite encouragements: *run like the wind* and *run to make the day your own*.

After the session Coach and I lay in the middle of the oval and stretched where the sun still shone. We saw the bright clothing and distant chatter of figures flitting in and out of obscurity up on the track in the bushland. I lay on my back and arched my head so I could see the upside-down horizon towards Rushcutters Bay. The sky faded from blue to white towards the horizon and as I filled my gaze I recalled a paradigmatic sky-gazing experience when just like today I lay in the middle of a grass oval and felt a rare sense of being contained and insulated by the great blue above.

On many similar occasions I had looked to the sky for similar feelings of sustenance but had merely felt exposed and disappointed or at best awed and excited. There wasn't that feeling of protection and sustaining intimacy.

As I lay there with Coach Fitz these elevated feelings returned, the sky at once massively distant and so close it was like a pod or blanket I could draw over myself.

I may have been right to presume Coach was feeling similar things as she lay there in the grass, head arched back and hands propped up by elbows, dangling just above her chest as though they were the redundant appendages of an ancient reptile.

We hydrated ourselves and performed pre-pub ablutions in the change rooms of the oval, noting the decorative ironwork in the small grandstand where the letter T was represented in a series of circles just underneath the awning. The corrugated-iron roof sloped downwards in a gentle curve I could imagine sliding down, the lip generously lifting me out into the air above the oval, where I would land sprawling in the soft grass.

Coach had replaced her training outfit with a pair of stonewash denim jeans and her blue blazer. We walked the backstreets behind the oval in the last of the daylight, noting the large number of art galleries still illuminated, and the sense that the area was cut out of the large sandstone hill that rose up behind it. The Moreton Bays and the looming blond cliff seemed to engulf the diminutive rows of houses, and both Coach and I agreed that the place was characterised by a gritty dampness, which she expressed by rubbing her thumb and forefinger together.

We found a set of inconspicuous stairs that led us to an elevated alleyway from which we inspected the roofs and backyards of the houses below. This slightly raised vantage, where houses ate into the still-abundant bush, seemed like the perfect spot to set up camp and I wondered whether in the future I might have the means to lay claim to a small patch of land in the area, settle there with the love of my life and raise a number of virile and sensitive children who might make their own forays into the bushland during the day and have it enter their dreams during the night.

We arrived at the bottom of a quiet street with a pub on the corner. Upon entry it felt as though we had been transported from the empty, dreamy, gradually darkening backstage of the suburb to a focal point of conviviality and warmth.

The establishment appeared to attract the polite and generous patronage of the local inhabitants. A group of middle-aged men sat at the bar, one of whom had a parrot perched on his shoulder. Everyone was excessively apologetic as we shuffled through the crowd to a free table and stools by the window.

After we bagged our table, Coach shot off to the bar to order some beer. I looked excitedly through the menu in her absence, immediately singling out the salt cod brandade and a side of vegetables with miso butter as my likely orders. When Coach returned she spoke effusively of the onion and liver jaffle she liked to have without the onion. Since our last meeting, I had started to suspect Coach's judgement about food to be less well honed than I originally imagined. It wasn't that she always misfired – this pub was clearly a gem – but her enthusiasm about the specificities left me perplexed. Perhaps I could rely on her to do the initial groundwork, to find a decent spot, but once inside it was necessary for me to go my own way. I ordered the salt cod and Coach proposed a toast to a well-earned meal.

I asked Coach about her favourite buildings around Sydney, wondering whether there were any in particular that catapulted her into the fervid displays of architecture-spotting that she now asserted as one of the great advantages of living in a city.

Well, she began, the exemplary architectural substance of Sydney, if it can be called such a thing, is perhaps to be found in the suburbs. Many have been realised in a far from ideal fashion, guided often by entrepreneurial demands, which are at their best when mixed with other sentiments, broader in scope and with the intention of more lasting benefit. The suburb allows the staging of bush and city, or at least it ought to, and in that combination the experience of dwelling expresses itself most vividly. The true suburbs of Australia, said Coach, are in Canberra, but Sydney too possesses some praiseworthy examples.

One day, after a run down to Botany to retrieve some bread rolls from a bakery I like there, she continued, taking a sip from her drink, I decided for some unaccountable reason to run back via a different route. Clutching my bag of rolls, I took a random, relatively unflattering track past industrial estates and across the railway line.

After some time I ended up in an area that struck me as distinctive, subtly so at first but then I had a dawning realisation that something persisted there that was lacking in the previous streets through which I had run. For one, there were more trees: large casuarinas and eucalypts shaded the streets in long avenues and haphazard clusters. The roofs adopted a form that seemed vaguely expressionistic, a slightly more adventurous yet at the same time unpretentious realisation of the Arts and Crafts principles that characterise many Sydney suburbs. The roofs jutted and spanned, creating areas of cool that were further augmented by spilling plants. There were the colours too: subtle lashings of gelato pinks, yellows and greens were applied with a recognisable degree of uniformity across the suburb. There were no front fences, which had the effect of highlighting the presence of the mailboxes that seemed to spring up out of the dirt and decaying tree matter. The lack of fences also meant that in some instances the contents of the front yards encroached on the pedestrian area, creating a happy confusion between the public and the private. Looking at the front yards, I got the sense of long-term occupation, with some featuring elaborate stacks of statues, pot plants, cacti, homemade signage and other ephemera.

I could tell that a couple at the table next to us had begun to listen to Coach. She spoke with increasing boldness and looked around as though performing for the crowd.

As I walked around the suburb I discovered hidden pockets of green, Coach continued. One internal reserve in particular awakened something profound within me, and I found myself pouring my time into wide-ranging and focused research on the idea of internal reserves and where the best ones crop up. This would soon lead me on trips to Canberra to admire the exemplary pockets of green in the suburbs of Reid, Forrest and Griffith, and then on further investigations into what I saw as the vaguely analogous though distinctive feature of the informal recreation areas at the fringes of sporting ovals, commendable models of which can be found at Alexandria Park or Waverley Oval in Sydney, or at Queanbeyan Oval not far from Canberra.

I followed one of the straight, long central streets to a park that functioned as a kind of apex from which several other boulevards fanned out, southwards to Botany Bay. From this view I was able to appreciate the sense of symmetry that informed the layout of the suburb and its pleasing contrast with the smaller, curved streets and the irregular forms of the houses and plant life.

I had the sense of something occupying my left periphery, and as I turned I almost jumped at the sight of a hulking, squat building that seemed to shoot straight up out of the neatly mown lawn. It was painted in the pastels common to the other buildings in the area, its slate roof partially colonised by patches of lichen. The softness of the colouring, the fancy roof vent and the mix of brick, sandstone and stucco, might evoke whimsy. However, in this instance, the almost aggressive solidity of the structure nullified any sense of the quaint. The four gables were brought together in a relatively tight form, creating a clash of different diagonal planes. An utterly unique sight. A prop forward of a house, said Coach, nodding towards me and the listening couple as though she'd composed this athletic metaphor after a good deal of mulling on the nature of the building and was pleased with her rumination's outcome.

As she talked, Coach had begun to peer over my shoulder in the hope that our food would manifest itself, and sure enough a young waiter strolled up to our table with our meals, thankfully resilient enough to shrug off a confusing remark Coach made about his accent and her great admiration for the Portuguese people.

I went to the bar to order another beer, and then we both set to work on our food, Coach making a good use of her fingers to prod and probe the jaffle, flipping it over on the plate after realising it was too hot, then taking a rushed bite anyway, chewing and looking at me with widening eyes of agreement while mine narrowed with suspicion.

The suburb I'd discovered was Daceyville, she continued, Australia's first public housing scheme. Its Parisian-inspired boulevards were once envisaged to extend all the way down to Botany Bay, an aspiration which has often brought me a good deal of comfort, despite its not being realised. Funding issues and World War I got in the way and only a small portion of the 1473 cottages planned were built. A publication at my local library and scattered documents on the internet give an indication of the difficulties builders must have faced erecting houses on what were essentially sand dunes. The sense of the landscape expressed in those images still persists to some degree if you look across the rolling treeless hills of Astrolabe Park and the Eastlake golf course at the south-western edge of the suburb. Part of me is transported to the stretches of sand that emerge through the grass and begin to dominate certain areas of Centennial Park.

These features enable me to feel I know where I live, said Coach Fitz. You need to seek a sense of continuity among otherwise disconnected regions of a city like this. Whole segments lie forgotten, never to be discovered, and the usual routes we travel can leave a meagre and often not very lively sense of the landscape as a whole.

From enclosure to enclosure we tread our routes, said Coach, sheltering from the sky in little burrows in the side of a hill. What we are left with, in terms of the landscape that exists inside, is inadequately fragmented and arrhythmic – a diagram of nodes or islands without animating force, without that fleeting though profound sense of the outside becoming a greater enclosure, built from partially stable though continually updated perspectives of the distant and recent past. My aim is to make the city my garden.

Coach was now talking as though she were addressing an invisible form taking shape above the table between us. I stand looking out over the scabby grass on the sand dunes of Astrolabe, I jog down that outer rim of Centennial Park, I cut through the remnant bushland of Fred Hollows Reserve in Randwick, or up through the moist gullies of Cooper Park and Tamarama. I hurl myself into a headwind on the soft sands of Bronte Beach, I witness my quads buckle with fatigue at the top of Waverley Cemetery, and as I continue to run I feel my body do what my mind tempts me to believe it cannot, and then I feel my mind in turn telling my body that it must simply get moving, stay moving.

Coach was tapping the outside of her almost empty schooner glass. We don't need chips do we? she asked, looking back over her shoulder at the bar.

I detected a restlessness in her that I speculated would only be quelled by a sustained session of drinking, a period of sexual intercourse defined by rigour and experimentation or, more agreeably, a night-time jog through the streets to some of the places she had just mentioned. She insisted I visit Daceyville for myself and meditate for a while on the degree to which it is a successful realisation of a garden suburb and compare it with other examples of its kind, such as Castlecrag or many of the suburbs in Canberra, and make a detailed account of my feelings regarding the lack of fences, the spilling front gardens and whether it seems appropriate to judge the maintenance shed as beautiful or ugly.

Despite the cool, welcoming atmosphere of the pub and the sense that the evening could, with the help of more schooners and snacks, be prolonged indefinitely and include a full session examining my romantic life, I thought it wise at that point to put a dampener on things and excuse myself, so Coach could be allowed to exercise whatever internal energies had stirred during this discourse on Daceyville.

I took note of this not infrequent desire within me to devise an escape route, a get-out clause, as though Coach was a bomb waiting to go off – or was it me, my nature, that dictated for every meeting I must have a ready-to-hand excuse for my imminent departure? Were my unfounded imaginings about her sexual being inducing me to read her gestures through the wrong interpretive frame? Was I guided by archetypes of desire and its realisation I'd gleaned from the entertainment culture that Coach so regularly critiqued? Did she want to have sex with me? Lay me out on the grass and stimulate my body with caresses and firmer gestures and then exploit this blood flow for her own satisfactions under the brown haze of the Sydney night sky? Would she sacrifice our functional, platonic relationship through a booze-induced display of uninhibited passion?

Either way, I was grateful that we were in a pub, so we'd already paid for the meal. I left Coach at the table, looking vaguely deflated and no doubt pondering another ale, or perhaps thinking to follow me out the door for a run in the night air.

For me, it was a reflective walk back to the Odyssey, to roll out the swag and sleep amongst the distinctive smell of Windex, citrus peel and damp towels.

During the night I heard a soft rapping on the window of the car. At first I tried to ignore it, burying my dehydrated head in a mass of clothes and balled-up bedding. But the noise persisted. I looked at the window and the shadowy outline of a face peered towards me. I wanted to yell but couldn't. I just stared at the outline with gradually building horror. The door opened. Coach's head snaked its way into the vehicle, a wisp of smoke, collecting above me and pinning me to the floor as it expanded against the roof. She clenched her jaw and frowned. I couldn't move my arms, couldn't speak. The fluid figure began to remove its clothes, revealing a set of breasts which appeared like two light bulbs glowing softly through matte flesh, and I found myself with my face pressed into them, sucking nipples sporadically and moaning as Coach inserted her fingers into my anus. A slick of sweat built quickly between us and I seemed to be in multiple positions at once: on the floor beneath her weight, my face in her chest and outside the car looking in as the fogged windows made our movements of pleasure legible in the glass.

I woke in a film of sweat, feeling as though I'd undergone an aneurysm in my sleep. The first of the day's light revealed thick white cloud, striated by the shafts of rising sun. I peeled off my clothes and got into my board shorts. It was with surprise and regret that I noticed a pale substance plastered through my pubic hair. I picked a path through the scattered boulders which led down to the waves crashing onto the beach. Warrigal greens and pigface filled the gaps between the sandstone and I could hear the sound of some wrens in the dense bitou bush up on the headland.

Walking down to the water, I began to give myself a hard time about my sex life. I hadn't slept with anyone since my experiment living overseas, and the expectation among my contemporaries was that sex, if it did not define your mental stability and worth, at least gave some indication as to whether you were making the right choices. Perhaps the path I had begun to tread led me to the same place as Coach Fitz: a solitary eccentric whose erotic life had been inhibited for whatever reason and then transformed into filial relations with various would-be athletes? My sexual desire was weak and irregular. I nonetheless harboured powerful and detailed narratives about a long-term partnership and the idea of a significant other borne along out there in the crowds of anonymous people, someone who also enjoyed the minor ecstasies woven through the routines of an ordinary day.

The water was glorious. I bathed and restored myself in my favoured channel that cut through the rock platform between

Tamarama and Mackenzies. I did some half-hearted aqua jogging and improvised aerobics in the waist-deep water. The swell was just big enough to send small waterfalls spilling over the rock ledge which formed the outer part of the channel.

I was reflecting on how different my chest hair looked when it was wet when a large dog, maybe a ridgeback, splashed into the water, pawing me with aggressive demands for some difficult to determine affection. I could hear its owner calling *Toby! Toby!* I managed to parry the animal's blows, and moved to its side where I could grab and pat it without being scratched. I'm sorry, said a red-haired woman, who, like many people that fascinated me on first impression, seemed a fusion of both adult and child. It's okay, I said, I love dogs, and dunked the animal into the water before pushing it away as I swam out into the wider part of the channel. The animal clambered out next to its owner and shook itself off before bounding away to sniff the rear of a French bulldog back towards the beach. Do you come here often? I yelled over the sound of sea – but she couldn't hear me and continued to look out over the ocean. Do you come here often? I yelled again. She looked at me, and said, What? Do you come here often? Yes, she said, it's a great place for Toby. Yes, I replied, it's one of the best dog-watching spots in Sydney. I sometimes come here with a picnic in the evening or at lunch and watch the dogs. It's better than television. She smiled and nodded before turning to ensure Toby wasn't getting into any trouble with the other dogs that were beginning to populate the rocks.

I put my head under the water and swam down close to the seagrass so it brushed against my face, imagining I was massaging images of Toby's owner into the perpetually growing stained-glass window in my mind. This is my private exercise, I thought, feeling the translucent leaves against my face, letting the odd bubble escape, thinking I could do this better than anyone. I looked up at the bright sky through the gelatinous opacity of the water. I was pleased to find the dog's owner still there when I resurfaced. I ejected myself from the water and walked over. My name is Tom, I said, still dripping from the water. Rachael. Toby is a lovely dog. Yes, he can be a bit of an oaf, but he's a good dog. I noticed I was scratching my head as I often did when nervous. I wish I had a dog, I said, but at the moment I live in my car. I think I'm going to move into a place soon. Good idea. Toby! Stay out of it. Come here. At this point Rachael removed a small soft pink plastic ball that had been hidden in her swimmers. It had a little face on it. Then she removed another, more or less exactly the same, except blue, with a few different appendages. She threw them both into the water. Due to some unaccountable compulsion I found myself sprinting towards the toys with Toby. I leapt as high as I could into the air and out over the water, perhaps hoping for a second that God would punch me at the apex of my flight, and then, *splash!* I pushed the dog to the side and retrieved the first toy and then the second, squeezing them in my hands to test the material. One made a dull squeaking noise. Toby was pawing me again, so I ducked under the water and swam back towards Rachael, leaping out of the water and handing her the toys. Toby joined us and we stood for a while with little to say. I noticed my palm was bleeding and with the blood emerged a vague memory of my dream. I held it out to show Rachael, who was occupied patting Toby. I thought it was probably a good time to leave, and I said goodbye, hope I see you down here again. Me too, said Rachael, trying to pry one of the toys from Toby's mouth.

Walking back up to the Odyssey I started to imagine inviting Rachael over to dinner at my new house. I would make fresh pasta with high-protein flour and a light sauce of chilli, tomato, basil and garlic, and maybe even have some ice cream for dessert. I looked at the Odyssey parked in a well-chosen spot under a tree. We've come a long way, my friend, I said, but it's time to move on, I need to have Rachael over for pasta. Rachael and I would sit in the garden after dinner and maybe we would edge close enough so our bare arms would brush up against each other. She might tell me that she needed to go home, but it wouldn't mean she didn't like me, just that she needed to go. I would walk her to the door and before parting I would ask if she minded if we kissed, and she would say no, that she didn't mind, and we would kiss beneath the door frame. We would say goodbye, Rachael suggesting we meet again soon, giving the impression that she really did have a good time. I would return to the kitchen to make a cup of tea, examining the contents of the evening to extract some kind of perfect certainty that I had said and done all the right things, and that she had been impressed and hadn't got the sense I'd been trying too hard.

Coach Fitz's Garden, Annandale

Only a few days after our discussion in the pub I was surprised to receive a text message from Coach inviting me to her house in

Annandale for a beer and some recreation in the backyard the next evening. Despite my hesitations due to the awkwardness of our last meeting and my ambivalent understanding of her intentions towards me, I overcame my apprehensions and resolved to go.

I parked my car on Albion Street and knocked on the door of an old weatherboard cottage. I received no response and repeated the gesture several times without any luck. The wooden gate leading up a tight alley to the backyard flapped open, having fallen stray of the broken brick that would hold it in place.

I cautiously made my way up the side of the house calling progressively louder hellos as I walked. The alleyway opened out into a paved area, behind which stretched a small lawn and a vegetable patch surrounded by medium-sized eucalyptus trees.

Coach was sitting at a large square wooden outdoor table with a collection of empty beer bottles and a metal bucket containing fresh, frosty beers embedded in ice. Behind her was a pigskin dartboard in a novelty medieval-style wooden cabinet, its doors ajar.

Six darts and an old baseball were arranged on the table in a manner that while appearing haphazard nonetheless seemed purposeful, and even before exchanging pleasantries I felt a compulsion to pick up a dart and connect it with some desired target in the vicinity.

When Coach stood to offer her hand I could tell that the beers had gone to work on her usually impeccable balance, a fact confirmed in her warm greeting, which was laced with a playful aggression that while often present in her voice had on this occasion risen to the surface in a more explicit, even malignant fashion.

My mind had already begun working away busily on its selection of escape routes. Darts? she said, which, considering the arrangement of elements on the table seemed like an inarguable proposition. We played a bastardised form of darts that Coach called 'golf', and unlike me she got steadily better as the grog kicked in further, each throw acting like an imperative to regain her composure.

After three rounds we had emptied the metal bucket of its beers, and Coach suggested we might try another game, this one involving various objects around the garden and the old baseball, that she had improvised on a previous evening. The gist of the game was to hit objects on the full with the ball, for which you were rewarded with maximum points. Lets call it *ballie-ballie-thing-thing*, said Coach, scanning the yard for appropriate targets. She nominated a besser brick, a lemon-scented gum, and the 'swanny man', a gnome-like statue of a football player in red and white standing guard over the vegetable patch.

Coach went first, and she hurled the ball with such force at the besser brick that when it hit the target it ricocheted over the wood-paling fence and into the neighbour's backyard. She looked at me, seeming at once exasperated and entirely satisfied by the result, before scaling the fence and almost immediately popping back again, ball in hand, as though this was a routine she'd had some chance to perfect.

The game continued in this fashion, with balls flying everywhere and gestures of the victorious and the defeated becoming more elaborate and desperate as the refreshments wove their way through our bloodstreams. When we reached the swanny man in the silverbeet, the scores were locked. We had three throws each at the target and both missed our first two. On her third throw Coach's nonchalance obscured what I suspected must have been a fair amount of effort, because the outcome was a shattered swanny man, its hollow form amounting to very little once smashed into a pile in what was fast becoming a ruined vegetable patch.

Predictable peals of laughter were followed by the realisation that the game must now be forfeited and that we ought to retire to the table and perhaps to more darts, Coach with a sense of increasingly tunnelled certainty, myself willing but not without some concern as to where all this might be heading.

I did wonder whether Coach was merely using these games as an excuse to drink more, and that I was simply an accomplice and spectator called up to make the routine appear less grim. My mind turned over the possibility that at some stage during the evening I might force some kind of confrontation regarding the contradictions becoming ever more explicit between Coach's thoughts on maladaptive practices for ritualised transcendence and her current display of infantile jubilation.

Two different possibilities were held in balance in my mind: one, that Coach, like lots of people, was unable to gain an adequate grasp on her own shortcomings, which she was aware of in a sense but which didn't agitate her as they did when she observed them in others. Or, two, that Coach was totally aware of her own tendencies and through the application of a convenient pragmatism she had excused or trained their necessary eruption into relatively innocuous solitary displays, balanced by a varied schedule for exercise and inspiration.

Once we sat down I could tell a lengthy pep talk was on the cards. Tell me of your failings, said Coach, tapping the table as though her finger were identifying the question on its surface. What are your most profound failings? Why is it again that you have come to me? What is the source of your wish to improve? What keeps you up at night? She spoke as if she'd entirely forgotten everything we'd discussed up until this point.

For a while I scanned through possible responses without any success, turning to this or that story I'd already mined for its sense of pathos. Coach stood and positioned herself somewhere behind me, continuing to offer variations on what was more or less the same question. After the anxiety produced by her initial directness departed, I found myself beginning to discuss the period of dissolution in Sydney which was the initial provocation for my overseas trip. I decided I might acquire a sense of purpose elsewhere, I said to Coach. The west coast of Spain, to be specific, free from the stresses that led me into the same patterns of delight and sadness in my home city.

A common dream, came Coach's voice, a common dream.

I played things poorly on my trip, I continued, and managed to embed myself in a situation very similar to the environment I'd sought to leave behind in Sydney, as though I carried the capacity for my own failures with me, and inflated them to live within as soon as I had the chance. I met with old friends who, though it was unknown to me at the time, were the source of the joy and sadness that have given my life in Sydney its particular emotional tone.

One friend in particular, her name was Alex, became the source of an intense romantic investment. Buoyed by the idea that a new me might flourish in this foreign environment, I applied myself to the task of persuading her affections with diligence, and presented a character free from its previous inhibitions. No more would I hide my thoughts in favour of pleasing others. I outlined my position on issues regularly and took those in our small group to task when I believed they deviated from principles I held to be worthy. I wore striking mesh shirts I'd dug out of op shops and applied makeup to my face and nails. I perfected dance routines of a peculiar rhythm and performed these at every opportunity, often provoking others to circle and watch my antics. I learnt the lines of songs and poems by heart, and adorned my wrists with trinket bracelets of blue stone and silver figurines. I shaved my head and attempted to sustain a front of emotional generosity in contrast to the twisted being I imagined I'd been before.

This charade soon ended, I said, when I found myself in a position of having something to lose, when my efforts to attract the attentions of Alex proved fruitful, much to my surprise. It was your Arab Spring, said Coach Fitz. I set my tent up on the rooftop balcony of the apartment which Alex was renting with a friend, I continued, and started to hang around as though her presence was the oxygen I needed to sustain myself. I became risk averse, sensitive to the idea that a false move might offend. I began to expend energy on interpreting inconsequential gestures as affirmations or negations of a potential future together. I made what must have seemed to her a shocking shift from a virtuoso and vagabond, free from needs, polite and yet immune to bad affects generated by the scrutiny of others, to this peculiar being who wished to inhabit a stable, conservative domestic arrangement.

We parted ways for a while, promising to meet up again in London, where, after joining her parents and siblings who were renting a house there on an extended holiday from Australia, she planned to move indefinitely. Ah, said Coach Fitz knowingly, the second of your great mistakes. This, I concurred, *was* the second of my great mistakes. I attempted to live in London for what, in comparison to the impression it left on me, was only a very short while, maybe six weeks, I now find it hard to say. I tried to make a go of the relationship that, with the help of the city, seemed to reduce my self-esteem to such a degree that I was forced to build what some might consider too close a relationship with my internal voice, as though it were the only source of structure and comfort in an increasingly unfriendly environment. You didn't yet have a resilient repertoire of solitude techniques! said Coach. I couldn't get a grip in the city, I continued. I spent my time aimlessly wandering the streets, not really animated by the things I saw, preferring to sustain myself with cryptic sentences in a black leather journal which also functioned as a wallet and an archive for ticket stubs and other ephemera. I retraced the same routes to parks that I'd chosen for no particular reason and would sit there in the late summer weather at a loose end, a man stripped of his program. I bought an electric shaver to trim my beard. I bought a special kind of shampoo for my itchy scalp. I tracked down a few friends that were in the throes of their own problems. Utterly skint, my daytime diet consisted of a strong coffee in the morning, then bananas, capsicums and nuts throughout the day, sometimes keeping my hunger at bay with another coffee in the afternoon. Due to my lack of money and ineptitude at finding work, I was forced to sleep opportunistically at the houses of my partner's friends. When her parents left the city, I would stay with her in the house they had rented for the summer and wash my rucksack of clothes in the biscuity, lemon-fragranced powder that I came to associate with the city, spending the day shooing insects from the house and conceiving dinners of chicken and late-summer vegetables that would make my presence a more appealing proposition. When her parents returned, I would pack my backpack, joggers slung on the outside, books still riddled with sand from the beaches of Spain stuffed down the bottom, and escape before they arrived. Then I'd scrounge out a night of accommodation somewhere else, perhaps paying for a shared room in a hostel, sleeping on the bedroom floor of a friend, or even on a couple of occasions sleeping under the bushes of a nearby private common, putting myself to sleep with a series of nausea-inducing cigarettes.

Alex seemed to evolve in the opposite direction. She developed the active lifestyle and outgoing attitude that had been one of the reasons I was so drawn to her originally. She began a militaristic routine of morning runs before work and gym sessions in the evening, and became fearsomely committed to establishing networks of friends in the city. The levels of pride she had in her own family seemed to increase, and I could say nothing of consequence in any conversation that made my own legacy seem important. All our dialogues were oriented around either her birdwatching dad, hard-working mum, eccentric younger brother or a cast of ambitious, stylish, witty, cosmopolitan friends. I merely had my diary, to which I turned in her absence during the days. It might seem like an odd thing to notice, I said to Coach Fitz, but her eyeballs became strikingly clear and whenever we talked I inspected them distractedly, marvelling at their brightness and transparency, in comparison with the dull glaze of my own, which I spent increasingly long periods inspecting in bathroom mirrors.

Without work I had no injection of routine to give form to my days. I didn't run or use outdoor gyms, nor did I find myself able to show any interest in the built environment. I lacked mediators to open up the city for me. You experienced the city in a suboptimal fashion, said Coach Fitz. I existed in the bubble of an improbable love, I carried on, which I sought to maintain in good part due to its improbability and the legend I had concocted for myself that showed its unlikely evolution.

Without my noticing, Coach had replaced my previously empty beer with another, as icy cold as those we first enjoyed from the bucket.

It was as though I'd rescued something rare, an improbability, I continued, and that was a reason in itself to nurture it. I had set myself the challenge to obtain a dream and worked away hard, ruining any sense of perspective, any grasp on what a self-respecting individual might do in such a situation.

I recall sitting in the empty house of one of Alex's friends. I was confronting the dawning realisation, still not quite able to admit it to myself, that I'd lost sight of myself. I had overstayed my welcome. I was the residue of a holiday in Spain who through determination and finite resources of charisma had managed to keep a possibility alive longer than seemed likely. Now, in this new life, in this new city, without the means or the initiative to reinvent myself, I was starting to become an irritant.

I sat at the table in the living room scrawling absurd, self-referential sentences in my journal. A purple balloon that had been slung up some weeks before for a party popped loudly in the silence and shook me to my bones, my scalp beginning to itch on cue. At which point I realised I needed to leave that city. I had become very vulnerable, lacking the network of friends and familiar sights that would reliably remind me that I lived within them as well as within myself, and lacking motivation to stimulate my body and mind through exercise and exploration of my environment.

During my confession to Coach the late afternoon had become that time just before night where the sky bears the last traces of daylight and the solid forms of things became dark, vague, silhouetted shapes. Coach was standing somewhere just beyond my field of vision and as I turned to face her I discovered she was tossing the baseball from hand to hand in a fashion so gentle it barely generated a sound. She disappeared inside the house and returned with a bottle of gin, two bottles of soda and some lemons. I hoped Coach might at this point have some wisdom to offer as to whether my analysis of this situation seemed accurate and what might be the best plan of action for me to take regarding my romantic life in the future. But her eyes were glazed over.

Feeling my inhibitions lessened by the drink, and sensing I wasn't going to get any deep insights relating to my own romantic troubles, I thought it might be a good opportunity to inquire about some of the discrepancies between theory and practice in Coach's approach to training and living more broadly. I asked her pointedly whether she saw some value in occasional Dionysian displays of excess and the reversal or abandonment of normal forms of order. She looked at me, eyes somehow suggesting a different being was now pulling the levers. You must have been…you must have been a dud root, she said, grinning maliciously over her glass. We need to get you into the bedroom. Need to get you a little bit more loose. She picked up the bottle of gin and waved it side to side. I was stung and perplexed by this brutal, difficult-to-interpret joke, which hit me as exactly the kind of response Coach had critiqued so passionately during our previous discussions. I was struck by the sense that she and I both were imposters, drunken strangers rehearsing a routine that had lost its meaning long ago.

Coach stood up abruptly and disappeared inside again. I wondered whether now was my chance to leave but my initial offence at her response had settled, and something in me wanted to escalate the situation, to have it out. I looked up at the yellowy-grey clouds and the fragments of browny-black sky behind them, the ghostly washing on the small clothesline near the wooden fence, which was covered with a thick topping of unruly jasmine, and an upturned wooden chair on the lawn, which though motionless gave off a definite impression of having just been thrown there.

I waited until my anxiety at Coach's absence and at not doing anything overtook my anxiety at the thought of what I might discover inside.

The kitchen opened onto a tight dining room almost entirely taken up by a long, cloth-covered table, the centrepiece of which was a vase filled with dried banksia and a stack of running magazines. Most of the kitchen goods, apparatus and produce were displayed on a series of open wooden shelves above the sink, a few items stashed in doorless cupboards below.

All the lights in the house seemed to be off, but enough light filtered in from the relatively bright night to ensure I could get a decent enough mapping of the surrounds.

I looked through the open doorway into a dimly lit lounge room. There was a three-tiered shelf ornamented with rocks, and an old radio cut into the wall that separated the lounge and dining rooms.

As I hesitated before crossing the threshold into the dim space, I heard a scraping noise from behind me, and noticed a thin strip of light at the base of an inconspicuous sliding door just off the side of the kitchen. I walked over to the door.

The fridge which stood by the door was covered in poem-fragments configured from those magnetised strips of words: *the unfinished pole hyperventilates / each rancid memory and miracle glows / festoon gigabyte banana / pouring out the olives and broken glass...*

I stood for a while outside the door, my breathing becoming increasingly apparent. Coach, I called softly, *Co-oach*.

I stood for a while longer. Then before thinking about it I found myself sliding open the door.

Coach was hunched over on the toilet, naked, a hand-rolled cigarette flattened on the tiles under her bare foot. She looked up at me and stood in the same movement and before I could flinch

I was part of an embrace: Ah, you've come, she said, half relieved, half indicating that I was fulfilling a prophecy, you've come.

As she tightened her hug I felt the coiled electricity of her abdomen and the two softer lugs of her breasts. My heels lifted ever so slightly off the ground and as she released I gathered my senses and backed quickly away, through the open sliding door, which I hit with my elbow, then through the door from the kitchen into the yard and back down the alleyway along the side of the house, hallucinating moans as I imagined Coach crumbling in a heap back on top of the toilet, folding her body back into the pose of slumber from which I now wished I hadn't had the opportunity to wake her.

Daceyville and Astrolabe Park

The next morning I peeled myself off the Odyssey floor and in the blur of the new day found myself on a trajectory to Astrolabe Park and the suburb of Daceyville.

The morning was already hot but I chose to ride with the windows up and the air conditioning off to sweat out some of the previous night's toxins. The heat, the residual feeling of tipsiness, and a melancholic, synth-heavy song on the radio formed a background for the beginning of my efforts to think through Coach's transgressions and my feelings towards her. Of one thing I was sure: our relationship had been profoundly altered. While I was resolved to cut off contact in the immediate future, I still needed to discover how to integrate her teachings into my own running practice and philosophy without forgoing all the progress I had made.

I lost myself in speculation about whether the compulsion to immediately visit a sacred site of Coach's in such a state, while my emotions were still raw, was the product of masochism, or a desire to take ownership of the knowledge she'd imparted to me by transforming it into something new. Based on previous experience, I knew it was unlikely that I would completely turn away from a figure to whom I'd shown affection in the past, and seemed probable that I would find a way to preserve an impotent yet expressive version of Coach in my mind, a character upon whom I could still depend to make sense of a particular kind of attitude that was undoubtedly an obscure part of my own psyche.

As the Odyssey lurched around the roundabout which marked the apex of Daceyville I immediately saw the building Coach had identified as the maintenance shed. As she had said, its form was at once menacing and whimsical, appearing as though it were a larger, bulkier version of a smaller building.

I turned off the main drag to the right, and into the sudden sleepiness of Daceyville's curving, difficult-to-navigate backstreets. I noticed two girls sitting at either end of a concrete balustrade in one of the sheltered porches common to many of the suburb's houses. On the ledge between them rested a bottle of tomato sauce, which led me to hypothesise that the object one of the girls was picking at with her fingers was a sausage roll or a pie. I felt pleased that they were in such a well-shaded area, with casuarinas and eucalypts as well as the roof offering ample protection from the sun.

I parked on Cook Avenue with the intention of exploring first the internal reserve Coach had mentioned and then the maintenance shed, before returning to Astrolabe Park where I aimed to do a short jog to promote further sweating.

As Coach had suggested, Daceyville was an instructive example of how certain landscaping limitations produced unmistakeable changes in the atmosphere of a place. The absence of front fences in the suburb provoked me to consider how strange their seeming inevitability was elsewhere in the city. I wondered how I might put into words the magnitude of the feelings produced from what might appear an inconsequential difference.

Some yards offered displays of statues and plants clearly meant to attract the admiration of passers-by, while others stirred unaccountably strong feelings of pleasure simply due to the fact that they weren't demarcated from the footpath, so that I might step into them with ease. Some of the open front yards were almost entirely taken up by large fig trees, and there was a general sense of the suburb being well shaded. Occasionally the footpath would lead to an open space behind a cluster of houses where chairs, raised beds of grass and pergolas were sheltered beneath the greater canopy of figs or eucalypts.

There was a general though emphatic sense of sleepiness about the place. Daceyville seemed neither prim nor neglected but somewhere happily in-between. There was charm here, with nothing smug about it. Much of the grass on the verges hadn't been mown and there was an air of messiness about the houses and the front yards, but still a distinct sense of pride. Some of the houses seemed like conglomerations of multiple dwellings, as though the terracotta roof of one had grown to incorporate surrounding structures.

All around, strewn across the sidewalk, visible through the ratty lawns and grinding in-between my feet and sandals, was the whitish sand which at once echoed the long history of the site and suggested some yet to be realised continuity with the future.

I located the paved path that led between two weatherboard fences pleasingly free from paint aside from one or two washed-out green or pink slats. Visible above the fence line was a teasingly low-pitched roof, almost horizontal, with bricks painted pink and powder blue.

The reserve nested by the surrounding dwellings was empty apart from a man dumping a small pile of rubbish at its fringes. A slight wind stirred the congregation of casuarinas at one edge into song and I strode out into the centre, turning slowly as I walked to achieve some approximation of a 360-degree view. I was moved to begin a light jog that was almost immediately halted by a cathead prickle finding its way into the region between my foot and my sandal and embedding itself in my skin. After this brief hiccup I continued, emerging out the other side of the internal reserve. The pain of the burr gradually deepened as I crossed the crescent into the park at the axis of the suburb. I wondered whether this was the most forceful realisation of an axial layout in Sydney, and like Coach had done I imagined the boulevards fanning out all the way down to the shores of Botany Bay and La Perouse.

I sought out the maintenance shed, my perceptual faculties readied by Coach's ecstatic description. The building I found stood rooted to the ground like the evidence of some remote aesthetic order, a startling combination of sweetness and hostility.

When searching the internet later I expected at least a few pages of tribute to the shed, maybe even an unpublished thesis about the implications of the building for the notion of an idiomatic Australian ugliness or how, in appearing at once cruel and kind, it might reflect something of the Australian character more generally, if such a thing can be said to exist. After all, I thought, there are fan pages for things as unlikely as Bubble O'Bill ice creams, sneakers and various obscure pieces of electrical equipment. But my efforts turned up nothing, only a few scattered photos on pages detailing examples of the Federation style.

I removed my sandals and ran shoeless along the tree-lined boulevard, stopping at the Odyssey to retrieve my lunch-making apparatus, then continuing barefoot to Astrolabe Park at the south-western edge of the suburb, where I sat in the limited shade of some casuarinas and set out my picnic.

I had my usual olive oil and a wedge of slightly stale sourdough, accompanied by almonds, dates, hard sheep cheese beginning to look a bit worse for wear after two days in the cool bag, fresh tomatoes, and a Tupperware container of tabouli.

I sat down to enjoy my lunch in the shade of the trees, looking out over the bare hills of the park, thinking that it looked like an abandoned fairway from the nearby golf course.

Due to my lack of cutlery my hands quickly became covered in a film of oil, with flecks of tabouli and breadcrumbs adhering to the sides. I periodically licked my fingers, glad that no one else was dining with me to observe the spectacle.

A tall man with a smallish bulging belly in high-vis gear emerged in my peripheral vision and four dogs – two fat kelpies and two other barrel-shaped things slightly lower to the ground – began to scan the grass in front of him with their noses. Soon enough the little horde was over to inspect my lunch, and as the more adventurous barrel dogs came closer I was horrified to see that their skin-to-hair ratio was roughly the same as a scrotum's. They came close enough to warrant a stern warning and as they did so I noticed one had a distinctively asymmetrical face, with one eye bulging out to the side as if to obey autonomous desires while the other looked square ahead. Their skin was mottled pink and brown and the sum of their appearance and proximity became too much for me as I looked to their owner or minder in the hope that he'd call them off. He turned his head to face me, a silhouette in the bright light of day, and lit a cigarette, turning again to face outwards across the park. My disgust at the dogs was compounded by the sense of injustice that he was not only permitting his animals to harass me but also seeming to take pleasure in it.

I finished the half-sandwich that I'd put together and packed up my things, jogging back to the car with the implements rattling around in my carry bag. Despite this encounter I was resolved to see what the view was like from the top of the hill in Astrolabe and maybe inspect some of the vegetation clustered at the fringes of The Lakes golf course that I knew to be a rare example of surviving eastern-suburbs banksia scrub.

When I returned to the park the man was making his way back to his car, his dogs performing the last of their rituals against the temporary fence that bordered an asbestos removal operation at the eastern edge of the park. I skittered across the grass noting what seemed like the overgrown contours of sand banks or water features. The top of the rise afforded a view south-west to Botany Bay and the airport. The landscape was strikingly flat. The features of the golf course networked through the swampy vegetation that included thick stands of reeds, other water grasses and the twisted forms of low-lying shrubs, evidently battered by the strong southerly winds that would no doubt make their presence felt through this exposed region.

I returned to the Odyssey happy with the visions I'd captured on this expedition, though perhaps not yet feeling their full emotional impact.

That evening, I parked the car in a favoured cul-de-sac in Tamarama and settled down to sleep. I dreamt of unfamiliar dogs, ones neither from the park at Daceyville nor the farm at Molong where I grew up. But the setting was the cool of the back veranda at the farm. My cousin or uncle had died and my mum was forced to take these dogs on. I looked at them through the flyscreen window from inside the house, clustered on the veranda, one sitting on a wooden chair, its body facing away from me, its head twisted back, tongue out, panting with that vacant, expectant, but somehow gleeful look common to certain dogs. As I looked I wondered whether I might shoot them from my vantage inside the house or whether there was some less conspicuous way to get rid of them, maybe a curse orchestrated by nominating two rocks as avatars, placing them in the grass and burying glowing embers in the soil before each stone.

Solo Bowling: Cooper Park Nets

Over the late spring and early summer I sought to fill the absence left by Coach Fitz by attempting to perfect her plan for my practice. I became committed to the idea that through exceeding her ambitions, I could transcend the position of mentee in which her coaching efforts had left me.

This began with what I would come to remember as a particularly aggressive and successful athletic display at the Cooper Park nets, where on one of my earlier runs with Coach I'd spied the outstretched limbs of a leafless jacaranda. This image lay dormant in my memory only to be activated when I noticed that the jacarandas around Sydney had begun to flower. I knew immediately that it was time to go back and revisit the nets with my leather cricket ball, which I typically stored in a cup holder in the Odyssey. I waited until a particularly hot spring day so I could be sure that the drying vegetable matter beneath the nearby trees would begin to give off the sharp, vaguely sour smells I associated with the coming of the Sydney summer. In such an atmosphere I hoped I might reach a state of calculated delirium which exercising under heat duress could induce.

I parked the Odyssey on Edgecliff Road and picked my way through the gradually climbing backstreets of Woollahra, noting the numerous revival styles and ample gardens, including a massive, lavender-coloured house on a corner block in the Spanish Mission style, and a less commanding mashup nearby of Sydney sandstone, red brick, and the dark exposed beams against white plaster characteristic of faux-Tudor style.

As I reached the flat grass playing fields that stretched up the gully to the nets I felt a spring return to my step. From past impressions of Coach's running style and from the metaphoric work of my imagination I had taken up the image of a coil or spring, as well as related forms, affects and sensations to do with tension and potential, which seemed to contribute to the ease and delight that I experienced eating up the distance between myself and my destination. At the nets I flung off my shirt and laid it down at an appropriate spot on the pitch so I'd have a target to aim at. I began slowly, going through the motions like a ballerina, completing my bowling sequence without letting go of the ball. Then I bowled some gentle deliveries, spraying the odd one down the leg side without worrying too much at this stage about accuracy.

I focused on integrating stretches and stability into the bending and folding of my body as I stooped down and picked up the ball. After each delivery I would jog to the back of the net where the ball had ended up, sometimes lying for a while on the turf and pulling my knees into my chest, or, as I began to work up some steam, exchanging a few playful jabs with the black rubber that covered the lower part of the mesh net.

At the top of my run-up my entire being gathered around the rough leather ball resting between my index and middle fingers. My duty was not simply to bowl the ball at the stumps but to give it its best chance to be a difficult delivery for the hypothetical batsman at the end of the wicket. I am capacity-building for the ball, I said to myself, with more sincerity than sarcasm. This meant not overextending myself, which would cause me to depend too much on arm speed. Instead I thought of the action as the sum of the entire sequence of movements, beginning from the moment I looked down the wicket before my run-up and ending when I halted to a shuffle well after I'd released the ball. I grew more sweaty and everything seemed very involved with breathing and heat. The ground at the end of the synthetic wicket had worn down to sandy earth, busted-up rhizomes and small rocks. My stamping or scraping this ground in the manner of a bullock took on the air of an ablution, contributing to the overall rightness of my enterprise. After about twenty minutes two English tourists arrived to practise in the net nestled against the slope on the other side of the field. I bowled for a while before plucking up the courage to go and join their session.

Both were in their early twenties and the bowler had tousled blond hair and the general air of a brickies' labourer. I couldn't see the batsman behind his helmet.

I took a very relaxed approach for the first few deliveries, focusing on line and length. When I saw the batter was of some ability and that no fun would come from bowling without risk, I began to push myself further.

At the end of my run-up, before I bowled, I focused on a sequence of ideas that produced specific repercussions for the way I conceived of my body in space. Key among these was attending to my sense of balance, which Coach had described as 'the confederating sense' that brought all the other senses together. I did this by imagining my body as large and stable, a feeling I activated by focusing on the way my feet connected to the ground and gave me support. This sense of stability extended beyond my body, so that the distance between where I stood and where I needed the ball to be was seemingly reduced. Bowling became less a matter of shooting the ball as one might a projectile and more a matter of placing it where it needed to be in space, inserting it into a field of possibilities where it could do its good work.

As my anxiety at having joined a new group of people diminished and my ability to harness the advantage of this introspective technique increased, I began to trouble the batsman greatly, causing him to jump about nervously on the crease as my deliveries reared up in the manner of a cobra or a deep-sea fish lurking in the sand. Once I struck him in the ribs, causing him to double over while his friend joked and congratulated me. This was followed by two fuller deliveries, both of which rattled into the steel stumps. At the end of his innings the batsman also offered his congratulations and at their invitation I decided to stay on and bowl some more.

The heat of the sandy earth through my feet and the sense the bush gave of imminent conflagration further encouraged me to cast off any inhibition. I bowled as though I had the ball on the end of a string. After feigning confidence initially, the new batsman soon showed signs of discomfort. In the way he doled out advice he seemed to be the authority of the two, and I began to feel a touch of sympathy for him. But even as I tried to restrain my aggression I continued to trouble him with variable bounce, in particular sharp movement away to the off side. My willingness to inhabit the virtual realm was for once affording me success in the real world. I could visualise in intimate detail the trajectory the ball would take, and allowing it to do so became as simple as turning a switch.

My shaming of these two interlopers left me so filled with elation that I saw no other option than to run barefooted to Redleaf Pool, on the harbour beneath Woollahra Library. With sunscreen and sweat running into my eyes and my entire body throbbing with heated blood, I could hardly imagine a better way to spend an hour.

I took off, bidding farewell to the tourists, who looked on agog as I sped across the playing fields through the backstreets of Double Bay, which now brought memories of previous performances against visitors in cricket nets, and the general sense of levity I felt whenever moving across a wide, grassy expanse.

At New South Head Road I took the gently sloping wooden ramp through Blackburn Gardens down to Redleaf Pool, on my way passing a man with an oiled brown body, mirrored aviator sunglasses and sparse though long electric-blond hair. An assortment of fluorescent clothes lay next to him in a pile and he seemed to be muttering phatic ephemera gleaned from overheard conversations. His pose mirrored a Roman gorging himself on grapes at a banquet, though instead of food he imbibed smoke from a cigarette, and with every exhalation seemed more at home in such a public space.

I continued on, now under the generous shade of the fig trees and pines. At the water's edge spread an array of glistening, gorgeous bodies, stretched out on towels, inflicting their music on the surrounds, discussing the effects of the weekend and how they had attempted to remedy their various malaises with valium, coconut juice or green drinks garnished with cucumber.

I discarded my belongings and disappeared into the welcome cool of the water, fizzing with the newly available mental entities, as I'd begun to call them, that such a sudden change in atmosphere reliably allowed me to harvest.

After my swim I sat in Woollahra Library, reading the newspaper as well as a book about gardens and urban design. My preferred vantage in the library afforded views over the ample backyards of the house next door, known as *Elaine*. I sat and looked out over the tennis court, with its immaculate, sun-splashed grass, and imagined my ideal sandwich: a ciabatta roll, heavily oiled, with tomato, a few squashed olives, a sharp cheese and basil. I began to plot. In order to fill the void left by Coach Fitz I would continue her project. I would begin work on a series of thematically linked pieces of writing on the landscape of my city. I would develop a catalogue from ideas implicit in her talks' focus on features, styles and moods of the urban environment. With this in mind I began to compose a rough list of the themes that would organise my loose curiosity: outdoor gyms, stairs and athletics ovals; rudimentary enclosures such as grottos, gazebos, rotundas, caves, telephone booths, bus shelters and public toilets; favoured aspects and specific features like footbridges and internal reserves. I would intersperse my intellectual labours with increasingly precise inputs of strenuous physical exercise, usually runs of some sort, or strength work at an outdoor gym.

Internal Reserves of Killara

Scanning over the suburbs online I discovered Killara, on Sydney's north shore, featuring what appeared to be two internal reserves that might provoke a bout of extended contemplation and provide the material for my first topic. Judging by the map the two reserves appeared to adhere to what Coach described as the 'classic' form for internal reserves: a common green space directly encircled by the backyards of private dwellings, rather than by a road.

On a particularly rainy Sunday I took the train north, with a backpack full of bread and cheese, a sheaf of basil and a small vessel of olive oil. I got off at Killara Station and followed Marian Street to the Pacific Highway.

There was an abundance of lush vegetation, with large numbers of tall gum trees, gullies fringed by ferns and small palms, and a general build-up of wet bark, leaf matter and branches. The terrain was more hilly than the inner west, which along with the dense vegetation gave a sense of things crowding in. The fuzz of the steady rain against my hooded coat further heightened the sense of immersion.

It would have been easy to miss the entry to the first reserve, Ticket of Leave Park, had I not been armed with my phone to show its location. It was marked out on the street by an anonymous metal gateway between two houses and a path in the grass worn through to dirt. It was as close to everything one might hope for in an internal reserve. The large back fences of some of the houses were the only blight on an otherwise perfect realisation of this particular form. I was confronted with a majestic stand of Sydney blue gums as I entered the park and I experienced that much sought after transition from the mundane to the sacred: from the pleasant enough monotony of the street front to this set-aside gathering of vegetal elders overlooking the yards of the houses which give form to the space.

I stood for a while in the rain and it became clear to me that the notion of a circle of dwellings built around a unifying locus spoke to some profound anthropological instinct which from that point on I ought to satisfy at every opportunity.

Energised by the first reserve's exceeding my expectations, I continued on in the increasingly heavy rain, the lower half of my shorts and my shoes now thoroughly saturated. The entry to the next reserve was as easy to miss as the first, marked out by an inconspicuous sign and a small diversion in the concrete footpath. Larger even than Ticket of Leave Park, Jinkers Green featured a lush lawn, less heavily treed than its predecessor and with a more varied elevation profile. A well-preserved patch of wet sclerophyll forest spilled out into the open lawn, a remnant of the once dominant vegetation that had thankfully been allowed to flourish.

I decided the dense bush would give me decent enough shelter from the rain for my lunch, so I began to pick my way carefully through the tangled undergrowth. The vegetation became increasingly thick. It gave me the sense I might vanish into its centre, which I imagined as a dark void patrolled by spiders and yellow-eyed birds. I reached a small cleared space carpeted by large sheets of bark. I lay down my rain jacket on the ground and unzipped my backpack. The heavy static sound of the rain was interspersed by the occasional louder plop of a droplet on a larger leaf nearby. I took out my ciabatta and began to perform what was perhaps one of my most impressive skills: cutting bread and other products in my bare hands without a board, outwards from my body to prevent crumbs and juice getting on my lap.

A friend once observed this and suggested, albeit ironically, that I ought to go on tour.

I assembled my sandwich, working quickly because of the rain: tomato slices, shavings of cheese, basil, olives and enough oil for a small car. After the blur of eating I lay back on the ground. I closed my eyes to exist only in the sounds of the rain and my breathing and fell asleep.

When I woke the rain had cleared. Although I couldn't be sure, I had the sense that it was just before dark. Had I slept that long? Mild panic set in and I quickly pulled together my things. I charged out of the bush to find the reserve now peopled by mothers and children in colourful clothes playing games, some children forming small gangs, while their mothers talked and gestured, others standing alone looking at small objects in their hands and seeming to mutter things to themselves about a world which only they could perceive. I put my head down and walked quickly back towards the exit of the reserve, noting the wet, lime-white branch of an adolescent eucalyptus that dipped down to chest height, the name Hayley cut into its bark.

I walked back to Lindfield Station in a mild sweat, noting further tracts of land devoted to the bush. Water was still rushing through the drains. Grand houses in the Spanish Mission style were intermixed with more humble suburban types built from red brick, with white-painted railings which led up to entrances above twin garages. The bush continued to drip all around, the glistening piles of bark and thick wet leaves at varying gradations illuminated by the low sunlight.

It was only from the safety of the train that I began to reflect on the peculiar sense of disorientation and the portents that are often produced by sleeping in an unfamiliar location. I recalled an otherwise inconspicuous scene from the movie *Scream* which had a forceful impact on my adolescent mind and continued to fascinate me. The scene involved Neve Campbell's character, Sidney Prescott, falling asleep on a couch near a window sometime late in the afternoon. The small town in which she lives is abuzz due to recent murders and a suspected serial killer on the loose. Emotionally bound up in these happenings, Sidney is further disturbed because it is the anniversary of her mother's death. Based on those details the atmosphere of the scene ought to be grim, yet seems almost a party, with the young school-goers provoked into saturnine celebrations. When Sidney wakes from her sleep it is dusk. She is alone in the house and the last of the day's light is fading. To me there was something more significant about the timing of Sidney's nap than the gruesome crimes committed routinely throughout the narrative. I'd found I would establish a subtle yet profound sense of place on the rare occasion in which I'd managed to disorient myself in an unfamiliar environment through sleeping in it, and often thought of making deliberate journeys to certain locations to let them enter my dreaming brain.

Moving House

As Christmas approached I took account of my financial and domestic situation. After several nights in a row of interrupted sleep, and a suspicion there was now more than one huntsman living in the Odyssey, I decided moving into a house was within my means, that it was a wise decision if I wanted to rest my body after the stress from training as well as be able to invite people over for dinner. The dream of living in my car had run its course and I had begun to hanker for an increased quantity of flat surfaces, space for storage, walls for artwork and posters, locations for indoor plants, and the sense of security that comes from thicker walls and immobile foundations.

I began the process of searching various websites, and put out a request on social media asking if anyone knew of anyone with a spare room in their house. Within a week I had three places lined up to check out, two through friends of friends, the other through an ad on Gumtree.

The first house was in Cooper Street, Surry Hills, the bottom room in a terrace. I was to meet James at nine on Saturday morning. We sat on the couch in the filthy living room while the theme tune to Mario Kart looped on the television. The house was dark and damp, even for a terrace. Numerous cockroaches moved about surreptitiously and small shards of broken glass were scattered on the brown tiles in the kitchen. In the tight, overgrown garden, the old outdoor toilet now functioned as an improvised pot for asthma weed and other anonymous plants typical of Sydney backyards. A litter of kittens and their mother scuttled out under the back fence into the alley. James spoke in a husky, rapid voice and asked me questions about my work and what I liked to do in the evenings. I could tell he didn't mind a beer. I had made up my mind already before the interview began, and crossed Cooper Street off the list.

The second house, in Stanmore, was rented by a friend of a friend on Facebook, Emma, and her boyfriend, Tom, both of them studying agricultural economics at Sydney University. They had an immediately endearing manner and served me a tea and scotch finger biscuit in the backyard. I didn't like the shag pile carpet or the largely bricked-over garden, but I could see myself living there. The bathroom smelt of geranium soap and the sound of aeroplanes overhead punctuated our chat. I had lingering concern about how close the house was to that of Coach Fitz, less than a kilometre away on the other side of Parramatta Road. I said bye to Tom and Emma, undecided.

The final house I inspected was on Edward Street, Darlington. Another terrace, more or less exactly the same structure as Cooper Street but far better kept. I met the older brother of a friend, Nick, who lived there with three others, Jo, Lachlan and Chloe. My room was on the second level, next to the shower. It looked out onto the narrow, but pleasant enough, backyard. I sat down and had a glass of water with Nick in the living room, where Jo and Lachlan were watching rugby league on the television and scrolling on their phones. I could smell garlic.

Nick and I went out into the backyard, which had an outdoor toilet and a shabby-looking vegetable patch which Nick excused by pointing to the lack of direct sunlight and the competition for nutrients from the large fig in the corner. Lachlan had converted a forty-four gallon drum into a barbecue and Nick said it made great smoked tomatoes. Out the back was an alleyway where the neighbourhood bins stood in disarray. I liked the surprisingly abundant canopy cover and the proximity to Redfern Station and the Glengarry pub. The suburb had a sheltered yet open feel, with a relatively diverse elevation profile. I began to hope Nick had taken a liking to me and enquired about his work as an actor. He had repeated speaking roles in various Australian television shows with which I was familiar, and was currently doing some performance and presentation workshops for corporates. We spoke about his younger sister Jessica, who was in Singapore studying public policy. When he mentioned that he planned to swim some laps this afternoon, I was only too keen to discuss my growing obsession with running. Showing me his phone, he introduced me to an app called Strava, a social media platform for athletes. It allowed you to record and share your training sessions with followers, he told me, and gave you a breakdown of pace as compared to other runners, riders or swimmers all over the world. I wondered whether Coach was on there.

Nick told me he'd get back to me by the end of next week. I said goodbye and pondered having a schooner up in one of the pubs on Abercrombie Street, but thought it might be weird if any of the housemates saw me in there drinking alone. Instead I made a beeline for my favourite falafel joint, Savion, in North Bondi, where I planned to sit with a newspaper for a while before going for a swim and a workout on the outdoor gym.

The moving process was relatively streamlined. I had my whole life in the Odyssey. I didn't know whether to add the few implements of cutlery and cooking apparatus I had to the already overflowing drawers in the kitchen. Instead I left them in the car for emergency picnics. On my first night in the house we got pizzas from Gigi's in Newtown and watched a film where Jean-Claude Van Damme played himself. Jo worked in a club as a 'door bitch' so she said goodbye to begin her shift at eight. Lachlan and Nick threw questions back and forth about Van Damme's earlier films, which American states they would prefer to visit and the best pizza restaurants in Sydney. I chimed in with the insight that I was glad we were so close to Brickfields, which was among my favourite bakeries. This led to a discussion about bread and bakery treats, as was my hope, and the conversation soon turned to plans for us to go on food safaris around Sydney.

At a point in the discussion Nick began to speak in an exaggeratedly posh South African accent, then made a seamless transition to performing as a character whose identity was unclear to me. Lachlan clearly knew the routine and began to laugh. But for me, said Nick, *for what I want*, Whale Bay would be perfect. He then switched roles and began to act out a dialogue: It's not Whale Bay, Mum, it's Whale Beach. Yes, I know, but for me, *for what I want*, Whale Bay would be just right. This went on for some while and I found myself joining in with the laughter as Nick got steadily more animated and began to gesture and walk around the room.

Things settled down again and Lachlan and Nick returned to their phones and occasional comments about the movie we'd all stopped watching. I found a Jamie Oliver cookbook I once owned on one of the nearby shelves and began to look through the pages and reminisce about some of the first meals I cooked from recipes in my adolescence: beef and Guinness pie, pancakes American style, the late-night fry-up, and, most formatively, the sausage bap with melted cheese and brown sauce, which I used to accompany with a can of cola after a heavy workout in the gym. It was a different diet to the lighter, more subtly put together Mediterranean food I tended to eat these days, but had nonetheless been a gateway into the delight and sense of agency associated with preparing and eating food.

As the evening drew on I didn't quite know how to extract myself from the conversation, perhaps in part because it had been so long since I experienced this kind of after-dinner sociability. Lachlan excused himself and continued to talk to Nick as he walked up the stairs. I took this as an opportunity to make my own exit: Righto, me too then, I'll see you tomorrow Nick. Nick had pulled out his phone and was scrolling through it on the couch. Righto mate.

I indulged for a while in the spaciousness and security of my new room: this space *for me, for what I want*, carved out of the great, contested, volatile mass of the world. I got into bed, pulled out my phone, and opened Strava, which I had downloaded after Nick had shown it to me. As I began to follow friends from Facebook who also used the app, I marvelled at the epically scaled and yet in a way spatially impoverished connectivity enabled by my phone, and the contrastingly isolated yet spatially rich cell of comfort where I would now sleep the night. Much to my delight I found Alex was an avid Strava user, regularly uploading runs around urban green spaces in London, places like Hampstead Heath, Clissold Park, Finsbury Park and Wanstead Flats, all of which began to glow with an increased degree of significance in my mind. After being starved of information due to her proud absence from other forms of social media, this new ability to observe her activities immediately reactivated memories: Alex getting ready to leave the London terrace on a morning run, decked out in a visor, hair in a ponytail, pellucid eyes hungry to unlock further reserves of energy.

I scrolled through Alex's friend list and discovered she was following her brother, Morgan. I tapped through to Morgan's activities, thinking they might lead me to the location of her family home near Centennial Park. To my delight, Morgan ran regularly in the park. The ten or so runs I scanned through always followed exactly the same track around the inner fence, entering at the Govett Street gates, and completing two loops.

I followed others too: people who had shown glimpses of athletic ability in primary and high school, people I'd bonded with in gym sessions over the years, people who I didn't expect to show an interest in training. I thought about searching for Coach Fitz, typed half her name, then deleted it.

In addition to augmenting my runs with the virtual audience on Strava, I developed a habit of listening to music while running. I discovered that music could bring almost complete relief from minor pain and top up my energy reserves for between five and ten minutes, after which its influence would fade out.

In the selection of tracks for my playlist I exercised my preference for a particular combination of tone, lyric and instrumentation. Usually this involved an androgynous lead vocalist singing lyrics that related to the unlikely overcoming of a certain challenge through emotional steadfastness or ingenuity. This was often but not always accompanied by synths and a reasonably grubby bassline. The tone was largely uplifting, though shot through with occasional but all-important notes of melancholy. The melancholy aspect of the songs tended to be recessive rather than dominant. The key part of the formula was some suggestion, however allusive, that the singer was overcoming a psychological or physical obstacle through great powers of will or passion.

This lyrical element needed to be accompanied by appropriately uplifting backing, often but not always electronic. Ideally it would seem that the singer was overcoming the obstacle through the act of singing. I would become utterly convinced by their voice as a source of great potency and participate in this potency to the extent that I could feel it or receive it in the right key.

I encountered a perfect example in a song released by Carly Rae Jepsen called 'Your Type', which I earmarked as the song I would ideally like to accompany the taxing climb up from the Coxs River on the Six Foot Track. The key lyric of the song was a line spoken from the perspective of a female vocalist expressing that they weren't the kind of girl 'you', the unnamed addressee of the lyric, would call 'more than a friend'. I interpreted this lyric as an imperative laid down to some imagined other, demanding the subject and singer of the song not be conceived as merely 'more than a friend', in other words, as less than a lover.

This line was one among many of the elements in the song that combined to produce a profound though ephemeral influence on my imagination which involved me taking the position of the singer in the song, feeling the efforts of someone to belittle me, and then transcending this limited conception of my potency simply by channelling the conviction expressed in the melodious voice. In the context of my training runs, it was the physical and psychological challenge of the run and an imagined audience of doubters that were attempting to belittle me: he is less than lover, less than a champion. A steep hill, or gruelling goal for my tempo, would be joined by an anonymous crowd of imagined disbelievers and become an unnamed, unappreciative partner in the song, who didn't value the capacities of the lover to their fullest extent, or in my case, athletic capacities. I became the vocalist, the protagonist, who sought to prove themselves through a steadfast display of agency, calling on and expressing secret reserves of power.

I resolved to listen to music on the Six Foot Track, in part a gesture motivated by what I genuinely thought would help during the race, in part a signal to myself that I was a runner with a degree of independence from my earlier master, who I imagined would disapprove of the idea entirely.

A Run Through Rosebery and Kensington

The knowledge that my runs were now being documented and shared in the virtual realm of Strava seemed for a short while to have a transformative influence on my running. I was building an assembly of spectators, imagined or otherwise, which included these new recruits made explicit through digital technology as well as the formative but still burdensome presence of Coach, whose expressed interest in the post-industrial landscape of Botany was no doubt in part the reason I chose the nearby Rosebery and Alexandria for one of my more memorable runs of that period.

I had a few specific targets in mind: the green spaces evident on the map at Turruwul Park and Raleigh Park, the looming religious structures on the only significant hills in the region, as well as Kensington Oval and Paine Reserve, which, judging by the online maps, were among the few islands of public green space in these suburbs besides golf courses, and seemed all the more enticing due to this isolation. From here I would head directly towards the coastline at Coogee, perhaps going via Randwick Environment Park, and then on to Bondi, where I would find myself some lunch, have a swim, maybe a beer, and catch public transport back to my starting point.

I began my expedition at Turruwul Park where I left the Odyssey. A couple of informative signs told the history of the park's name, which is likely an alternative pronunciation of Dharawal, 'the Aboriginal people whose area spread from Botany Bay south to the Shoalhaven River and inland to Camden'. A road separates Turruwul Park from the surrounding houses, and in this sense it fell short of the internal reserve in its exemplary form, as evidenced in Killara. It was still a pleasure to stride across the grass and inspect some of its trees, including a Port Jackson fig, an American cottonwood, a Washington palm, two English oaks and a Port Lombardy poplar. The amenity of the park was increased through the provision of public barbecues, a children's playground, tennis courts, and electric lighting at the base of some of the trees, which, as I imagined, would successfully highlight their magnificence of an evening.

From here I took the most direct route to a curious-looking street formation I'd noted on the map prior to the visit: a road more or less taking the form of a racetrack and looking as though it might enclose a portion of green space or peculiar public amenity. I soon discovered the oval road traced through a large 'resort-style' apartment complex at the centre of which was a sunken garden bordered by a few trees. Some incongruously grand sandstone steps led down into the garden which, due to its peculiar form, made me wonder whether it was once a dam of some kind. Warning signs depicting bodies flailing above water and text alerting residents to the dangers of the park in heavy rain seemed to lend further credence to this idea.

I circled the park in the hope I might be able to find an exit on the other side of the complex. A couple of staircases led me to nothing but fences, sheltered barbecues and vague memories of my year twelve trip to the Gold Coast for schoolies. I cut my losses and retreated, back out onto the public road, and took a more circuitous route to Kensington, wondering how all these doodles and dead time would appear to the people I hoped might view the run later on Strava.

Some way after crossing South Dowling Street I came upon an entry to another sunken garden, a more elaborate, less haphazard version of the one in Rosebery, employing formal design principles, such as prominent symmetry along rectilinear and radial lines, and a replica of some ancient ruins, in this instance sandstone columns, entablature and a stepped retaining wall, all set on a slightly raised lawn platform encircled by a sandstone border. The columns marked a stairway that led right up to the other end of the apartment complex, and as I sprinted up each flight of stairs I noticed water features running down the centre of the path and sandstone benches set in small avenues of trees by the wayside.

The path led fortuitously to an exit on the garden's eastern perimeter and I continued on through the streets of Kensington to the convent and monastery that overlooked the suburb. I made the most of the hill leading up to the buildings, attacking it with gusto and pushing through until I reached the impressive entrance of Our Lady of the Sacred Heart Convent, where I removed my shirt and stuffed it down the back of my underpants. The convent was a brick building built in the Federation Gothic style with a large terracotta-roofed central tower and two smaller towers capped in zinc-clad steel. The five front-facing gables featured elegant bargeboards painted white, gothic features that along with the palm tree created a heady, vaguely exotic atmosphere.

I circled the building, sticking to the soft lawns. The strong feelings I'd been hoping for stirred within me as I soaked up the mental entities afforded by this expansive patch of open, elevated, lush green ground. I was content to settle for what in reality might have been a deluded interpretation of the place as some kind of utopia, high above the sandy flats below.

As I jogged along, the rhythm of my breathing began to form a loose image in my mind and without consciousness of the decision I found myself once again chanting *hick-a-chee, hick-a-chee, ha-ha-ha*. I let a certain inclination towards this being develop as I ran along: it was different to the previous *hick-a-chee*, more aggressive, yet humorous, hyper-stimulated, outgoing, a protagonist. I felt a force in my neck, as though it were swollen due to some venom. I began to involve my arms in a peculiar punching-dancing routine, pounding the air and raising my knees high. I passed a group of young boys in uniform crossing the turf. One yelled an obligatory 'Run Forrest!' and without giving it a thought I pivoted, circled back, and ran on the spot before the three of them, exposing each to the full brunt of my sweaty, hair-covered pectorals and the peculiar movement I'd adopted. The more rodentlike of the three began to cringe and shield himself from view, another seemingly started to whimper, grabbing the arm of one of his friends and scurrying off towards the safety of the suburban streets.

After running around the oval at a steadily building pace I broke off and ran towards the monastery at the very top of the hill: the final crescendo in this collection of impressive structures. It was the grandest of the three, built in the gothic style from Pyrmont sandstone. A commanding sense of symmetry was evoked by its steepled tower, flanked by three dormer windows embedded in the glazed terracotta roofing on either side. I paused Strava and felt a rush to perform a more archaic variety of telecommunication. I knelt, then let my head fall to the ground, and for a while became totally immersed in a world of breathing, sweat and darkness, a peculiar force circulating through me which manifested in visions of gift-giving, unlikely victory, great feats of bravery and improvised yet successful meals for large groups of friends, paired perfectly with beer or wine. Crowds gathered around me to enjoy the produce and the performance of my athletic ability. I breathed deeply, rewarding my body, radiating generosity like some precious stone uncovered by desperate travellers on a journey to salvation.

After this episode I assessed the vantage to the east, across Kensington: the terracotta rooftops interspersed with figs, eucalypts and palms. Here I am, I thought, on this peak, clustered with grand buildings, enjoying the security and levity offered by such an aspect, and with these thoughts still reverberating, began my descent down the slope, for a far more subdued run around the suburban streets, now and again noting the sandy soil which, as Coach had insisted, indicated a cohesive, invisible landscape that recent human settlement had obscured.

Kensington Park was my next stop, and while perhaps not matching its namesake in London in terms of grandness, it did feature a picketed sporting oval fringed by some excellent trees, among which were included conifers and Port Jackson figs. I recalled Coach making specific mention of this combination of informal recreation area, in the form of treed fringes and gardens, and a well-kept sporting field. I made a note to add this typology to my list of kinds of places to be catalogued as I followed the concrete footpath that wound its way through the trees and through a series of circular sandstone garden beds, unfortunately populated in large part by asthma weed, though in some beds grew a soft grey-green plant that was like sheep's wool to the touch.

On the eastern edge of the park the Kensington Bowling Club was in a state of neglect. Longer grasses and yellow daisies colonised what would have once been a pristine lawn. A fine sandstone birdbath, made from a series of stacked, roughly circular pieces looking vaguely spinal, retained a degree of distinction amid the not altogether displeasing mess of grass. Signs indicated that a community centre, basketball court and, more worryingly, a large car park, were due to be built on the site. As I endured an unresolved internal debate of some intensity about the values of unkempt lawns and low shrubbery versus community services of the kind proposed, I soon found myself running across the old tramway of Anzac Parade, with Daceyville just to my south.

My next island of green was Paine Reserve. While not blessed with the abundance and diversity of trees featured in Kensington Park, it did appeal in some unemphatic but exemplary way. This might have been to do with the rugged quality of the sizeable rock outcrop and its raised aspect over the rest of the park. The exposed sandstone ridge, the single palm tree and the figs on the perimeter of the park converged in a selection of elements that for a vague reason provoked a hypothesis this was classic Sydney.

I took my bearings and headed towards the promisingly named Randwick Environment Park, which I'd singled out due to the presence of a curious circular marking on the map surrounded by remnant and regenerated native bush. The park was all that I could have hoped for. A rare tangle of coastal shrubbery through which a footpath networked, terminating in several viewing platforms from which I watched woodland birds dive and play like low kites, their distinctive sounds animating the atmosphere as though it were a stadium. The peculiar elliptic concrete pathway ringed an area of turf where families picnicked. The bushland formed a thick border around its perimeter, stretching up to the hillside, before gradually becoming populated with sensitively scaled dwellings, roofs partially visible through the branches of the larger native trees.

I continued on to the increasingly variable elevation of the coastline, running through crowds of beachgoers, first at Coogee, where on the southern side I took note of another rudimentary amphitheatre, in which I imagined I might stage a performance of some kind in the future: a chance to share my recent ecstasies and mundane rituals with a small crowd of valued acquaintances, or perhaps even a crew of devotees in the grip of the training ideas I'd inherited and developed from Coach Fitz.

I stuck as close as possible to the coastline and took the route up the northern headland, down through Gordons Bay, Clovelly Beach, Burrows Park and the majestic Waverley Cemetery, where, so Coach had told me, the namesake of Trumper Park was laid to rest. On the northern side, Coach had told me, was a slope well suited to repetitions of hill sprints, and I felt certain that in days not too far away I would subject myself to the rigours of that steep hillside, rewarded abundantly by the solemnity and grandeur of the setting and afterwards the cool waters of the Bronte Bogey Hole.

The expanse of ocean spread from my right to the horizon in front, culminating in the north headland of Bondi in the distance, where I planned to swim and feed myself at the conclusion of my run.

I headed onwards, past Bronte and Tamarama, both of which had attracted largeish crowds and were full of the sounds of reverie that accompany humans picnicking on the weekend. At Tamarama

I couldn't resist the temptation to grace the little oasis of Fletchers Gully with a series of stair sprints, ensuring that my quads where taxed to the maximum degree, before sailing through my final repetition without stopping to rest, as I had done with Coach Fitz, and continuing to Bondi, where, after uploading my run to Strava and checking whether I had received any kudos from my followers, I spent the afternoon swimming and uttering expressions of deep thanks to the climate and geography, demolishing quantities of deli goods, and finally hobbling to the bus station from where a sequence of buses and trains conveyed me back to Darlington.

Approximate Contact

I continued to check on both Alex's and Morgan's runs on Strava, and I was surprised about a month after the Annandale incident with Coach Fitz to receive a message from Alex, who had seen some of the 'impressive' runs I had been uploading. I mentioned my admiration for her efforts too, and told her as well that I had seen the routes Morgan had been running on Strava. In response, she confided in me that he seemed to be going through something of a rough patch and, from what she could make out from her distant perspective in London, in need of some guidance in his life, which must have seemed wayward in comparison to the disciplined manner in which she organised her routines.

I saw this as an opportunity too good to waste. I decided to offer my services as a coach, delighting in the desire to maintain a kind of surrogate contact with Alex through a being who shared some of her genetic material. It was even more meaningful than communicating through my running efforts on Strava. I had a vision of redeeming some of my past failings in London by transmitting my new, robust identity, across time and space, through the conduit of Morgan.

The importance of this initially flippant offer grew enormously when Alex, in full support of the idea, wrote back with her brother's contact details. I felt light-headed, my body temperature rapidly escalating, and I smelt a distinctive odour I knew to associate with stress. This was a profound opportunity, I sensed, to orchestrate a warped meeting of two contrasting yet in a way perfectly compatible desires: to share my emerging knowledge about the body and place with an audience, and to maintain and transform elements of my emotional history by bringing them into contact with an improved vision of myself. Yet there was doubt: I felt assured I was filled with the right information until confronted with the task of having to articulate this to an other who was interested but in need of convincing. I had never coached anyone before and doubts about my naïvety were magnified by my reawakened feelings of inadequacy, and I began to imagine Morgan's scrutiny of my coaching techniques as comparable to his sister's evaluation of my worth as a lover.

I continued to ruminate on my newly inherited challenge while performing exercise routines at Prince Alfred Park later that afternoon. A man and a woman occupied the chin-up bars, both in baggy but comfortable-looking white athletic gear. I assumed they were Russian due to a YouTube clip that I'd watched of Russian people doing elaborate exercise routines of a similar kind on rudimentary outdoor gyms. Both were strikingly beautiful and strong. I admired their twisting and balancing bodies as they curled meticulously around the bars and held themselves taut, seemingly able to manipulate their entire body weight through internally controlled surges of force. The man spread his legs wide, bent forward, touched the ground and began to jiggle his body. I watched the toned muscles in his upper leg vibrate and, in a gesture of camaraderie rather than competition, I chimed in with my recently evolved variation on squats, which, in addition to the usual up-and-down squatting movement, required that I continually shift my feet, so I gradually moved around the outer perimeter that cordoned off the equipment from the surrounding lawn in a rocking, bouncing motion. Each time I shifted a foot I was sure to focus on its prehensile capacities, as though it were grabbing at or maybe even licking the ground.

After the blood in my body had been sufficiently channelled by my exercises, and my head had been cleared of the residual tension produced by the stress and excitement of the challenges I envisioned I would face in 'Project Morgan', I stopped for a while to admire the remnants of a terraced, sandstone garden just near the equipment. The agreeable mood of the area was increased by the presence of two fig trees branching out like permeable walls to encompass the sunken patch of overgrown grass. I imagined laying out a picnic rug on the grass with some company. The figures in my mind were indistinct at first but gradually revealed themselves to be an ensemble of key characters from my past, the enduring and the temporary. We were gathered in an atmosphere vibrant with my own gratitude and forgiveness, free from anxiety and apprehension, clothed in loose, bright, comfortable linen outfits that didn't stick to our skin in the heat. At first a rug was our only piece of equipment, with the long grass flattened beneath its protective surface, then other items began to appear in the vicinity: a small wicker basket, piles of discarded clothing, plates with half-eaten portions of food and other plates with servings yet to be attacked, wooden chopping boards arrayed with cheeses and fruit, stacks of books, candles, pillows and sheets, an esky, stray cutlery, glasses of wine and wine bottles, a vase with a selection of grasses from the area, a small set of shelves on which sat neat piles of clothing, speakers, some pens, paper, and a small collection of rocks.

I scanned the faces of the cohort: my parents, my siblings, my dead grandparents, my new flatmates, friends from my past, Rachael and her dog Toby, Alex and the dimly imagined faces of her parents. There was Coach happily conversing with my grandfather, and lastly a figure of persistently obscure guise, a face that seemed to shift between certain fading memories of Alex and flashes of the runners in *Chariots of Fire*: a face of exuberant and shameless conviviality, focused and shaped in his disposition by routines of athletic expression and vague though forceful goals for the future.

Meeting Morgan in Centennial Park

In the lead-up to meeting Morgan, I thought about the kind of coach I hoped to be and wrote out a series of guidelines for my coaching style that were a synthesis of the insights I derived from Coach Fitz and various other occasions of inspiration and interest. I decided it was important to give whoever I was coaching the sense that I was speaking to rather than at them, and to speak from the heart, whatever that might mean. I thought it would be good to couple this earnest requirement with the contrasting ambition of irreverence, and to give my subjects the sense that while I was a straight shooter, I might also surprise them at any minute by discussing a taboo or giving a cutting though humorous caricature of some type. I resolved that unlike Coach I would allow Morgan more scope for input in deciding locations for runs, and try to appear generally less dogmatic when it came to expressing my views.

Despite this laudable intent I couldn't resist incorporating some architectural education into our next meeting, which took place on one of those increasingly frequent scorching Sydney summer mornings. Overnight there had been no purge of air from the heat of the previous day and by 7 a.m. it was already hot and humid.

Morgan was waiting when I arrived at the park. He was making a lacklustre attempt to stretch his quads, balancing himself with one hand on a tree, and I was glad to see that he too was perspiring.

Morgan! I interrupted, wondering whether I sounded jovial or zany. Tom! he turned and held out his hand. He was wearing a black pleather hat pulled down over his head, and his long, thick hair obscured all but the key features of his face. I could see small constellations of acne on his chin and jaw along with beading sweat and small bits of bumfluff, but the central features of his face, the eyes and mouth in particular, had a kind of purposeful brightness, which immediately activated a series of shimmering, barely conscious memories of Alex.

I suggested we do a light warm-up that would allow us to jog past the Rangers Cottage, where I could offer what seemed to me a relatively well rehearsed account of its style and architect.

The architect was Walter Liberty Vernon, who along with John Horbury Hunt and George Temple-Poole could be persuasively claimed to be among the first experimental practitioners of architecture in the new colony. Vernon practised a kind of proto-modernism, I said to Morgan, as the house emerged in the distance, in the sense that some of his buildings were adapted to the site and the climate rather than the reiteration of classical orders. He seemed entertained on some level, perhaps forcibly, so I continued with some other insights about how the bungalow form employed in the Cottage was arguably of more widespread and enduring influence than the much-hyped skyscrapers often thought to be synonymous with the twentieth century and modernism. As always during moments when I was imparting knowledge, I experienced a wave of uncertainty as to the worth of the information I was attempting to convey, and reminded myself of the many pitfalls that await the mentor given to too much lecturing.

We followed the steep but short rise up past the Rangers Cottage and down the sandy path on the other side. I planned a steady loop around the outer rim and then a faster lap or two of the inner loop, depending on how we coped with the weather.

It was clear that in these early stages of our relationship it would be me who was responsible for maintaining a sense of vitality in the dialogue, so I began to pour myself out into that silent space and talk about how it felt like my blood was boiling in the heat and that I was moving through a substance far denser than air. Morgan chimed in offering agreement and a comment about how he looked forward to the bits of shade offered by the trees, which offered enough to suggest it wouldn't be a constant battle to gain some semblance of engagement. We trudged along with our shirts darkened by sweat. I was feeling slightly buoyed by the responsibility of my new role, and wondered what character might be revealed as Morgan continued to emerge from his shell.

It was difficult for me to get a grip on the shape and dynamics of his body during the run. At first I thought his shoulders were narrow, then I decided they were broad. Were his legs slight or stocky? His stride and arm movement, more than any other runner I'd observed closely, suggested the movement of a bicycle, eating up the ground in some semblance of a circular motion. There was something utterly unnatural and yet perfectly fitting about it. I found myself imagining him in cartoon form with two large, spinning wheels mounted on either side of his torso.

After our first lap around the outer rim of the park we stopped at the base of a Moreton Bay fig where I had hidden a water bottle and a banana in one of its cavernous buttress roots on my jog over to the park. Unfortunately the banana had undergone significant bruising and was a day or two past its best. It had began to ferment, and I was forced to eat half of it out of the skin directly before making a lacklustre offer of the other half to Morgan, who refused it, so after taking another bite I threw the last quarter in a bush. I consulted with Morgan who agreed one more loop of the inner track ought to do it for the day. We'd aim for something approaching the pace we might hope to sustain for a half marathon.

We set off at a faster pace and before long I started to pull away from Morgan. I was wondering whether I should slow down so we would be running together, but before I could make up my mind whether to slacken my pace Morgan appeared again at my side, with a look of joy and determination that made me consider us partners conspiring against the inevitable and pervasive forces of entropy.

My growing familiarity with the park had resulted in stretches of track inducing different feelings of anticipation and expectation for my performance within them. As I passed through these I felt my body marshal or subdue its resources to correspond with the way I would imagine myself in each part. I mentioned this to Morgan at the conclusion of our run, where I'd adopted my habitual post-effort posture of putting my hands above my head and grasping the branch of a tree or, as was the case on this occasion, leaning forward on the trunk of the tree with my weight collecting in my palms, opening up my lungs.

It's almost as though my body subconsciously conforms to a virtual score orchestrated by the surrounds, I said to Morgan, who now mirrored my stance on the other side of the tree trunk before giving up and bracing the weight of his hunched body on the white painted-railing that demarcated the inner circle of the inner loop. He removed his hat, enabling a full view of the sweat streaming down the sides of his face and collecting on the bridge of his nose. His long hair was matted and dark at the edges. I felt the rhythm of my breath and the swelling and contraction of my body in the heat. I watched the motion mirrored in Morgan and examined how the demarcation between the skin of his face and lips had the same pronounced outline and curvature as Alex's. I thought of the earlier fantasies that had stirred within me about notions of genetic inheritance and the enduring marvel, at once utterly mundane and enigmatic, that some people were like other people and yet different, that the gestural presence of different beings was ghosted within other individuals, so that we are never merely singular but rather perpetually perishing collections of animated, psychological and physical events. I imagined Morgan as a kind of screen with its own autonomy under which the obscured presence of Alex and their shared ancestors constantly shifted, and how impressions of a different yet similar variety, the presence of Alex in my memory and imagination, shifted within me.

I examined these feelings more scrupulously in the Nelson Hotel at Bondi Junction, just near the uppermost corner of the park. I spent some of my early years in Sydney working behind the bar there, which had managed to retain more or less exactly the same aesthetic and atmosphere, despite the rash of new fit-outs that seemed obligatory for many pubs in the area. The staff seemed like different versions of my former peers, blond-haired and tanned and energetically servicing the same bus drivers who clustered at one segment of the giant oval bar, demanding immediate recognition of their needs, their drinks served in special cold glasses stashed in a corner of the fridge. I was surprised to find that their drinking habits did not seem to have aged them too severely.

I placed myself at a stool some distance from this mob and began to reflect on the surges of love I'd experienced when encountering certain younger individuals I identified as potential disciples. One such boy was the younger brother of a girl I had fancied at the school where I worked during my so-called gap year in England. Something of her energy was preserved in his appearance and as a result I found myself favouring him in the rugby team I coached, buying him vodka-and-orange mixers from the shops, and offering support at every opportunity. I felt a strong desire to protect and impress, yet there was none of the erotic sentiment which characterised my feelings towards his sister. I recalled this filial affection being encapsulated by a ridiculous Celine Dion song called 'A New Day Has Come' that was popular at the time. I would call to mind the refrain from this song and vague memories of its music video as I walked over the cobbled streets that led between my flat and the boarding house where I ate dinner.

My feelings for Morgan were similar. My intimacy towards him was in part a consequence of my still-resonant emotions about Alex, and yet these were feelings of a new variety, given form by a different teleology, which led to new possibilities for imagining: I saw myself as a figure dressed in torn, baggy clothing, somehow vaguely maternal, barefoot beneath a yellow box eucalyptus. The ground around the tree had worn to dirt and was peppered by the occasional nettle or tuft of horehound. Morgan's body lay motionless on the ground, wounded somehow by the villainous horde I was facing. I growled at them through my teeth like a dog as they attempted to get closer to his body. It wasn't clear what form they took: maybe animal, maybe human, maybe some merging of the two.

I turned my mind to activities that would further bind us through a combination of post-exercise chemical reward and the sense of curiosity developing from insights about the urban environment. Before parting in the park I had proposed a weekend run along the green fragments that remained between the Tamarama stairs and Centennial Park, after which we could return to the beach for a swim. Morgan, who I sensed had a relatively indiscriminate attitude to my suggestions, said that'd he'd be able to do it if we finished before lunch.

Then, to ensure the steady progression of our relationship, after the Tamarama run I would propose we meet in Castlecrag, something of a paradigm suburb I'd meant to visit since Coach mentioned it in the pub after our Trumper Park session. Here I would be able to reach a supreme level of eloquence as I moved among the area's unique houses. Morgan would begin to see me as an essential part of his development and I would atone for my inability to derive a sense of purpose from my surrounds during my stay in London with his sister.

Tamarama Gully, Waverley Park and Centennial Park

Morgan and I met at the base of Tamarama steps on a particularly muggy day. I had the intention of doing ten 400-metre repetitions around the Waverley Oval after a warm-up jog along Birrell Street, beginning at the steps. Then, depending on how we were feeling, we could do some sprints up the more modest but still sizeable stairs leading to the reservoirs on top of the hill in Waverley Park. I imagined Morgan and me admiring the view eastwards towards the ocean from the top of the hill. We would have sweat patches collecting on our bodies and be ripe with new ambitions relating to the further refinement of our physical capacities.

Morgan arrived armed with a large water bottle, his face coated in sunscreen and entire head obscured beneath his black hat. He greeted me reticently, while still giving the impression he was excited about the run. It was impossible not to think of my previous session with Coach Fitz at the steps, and the detailed description she gave of the history of the gully and the relationship between the past practices of amusement on the site and the more sober forms of self-sculpting she championed. I didn't attempt to reproduce her level of detail or emphasis, but I did mention the fact that the beach used to be the site of an amusement park and, mirroring Coach's words almost exactly, said that today we would seek out our own form of recreation, slightly different to those people who once sought amusement in rides and costumes. As soon as I said these words I felt myself shudder at the feeling of pretension I now associated with Coach Fitz. I felt compromised by the idea we were practising something more noble than play, and wondered if the tension between this hesitancy and the elitism that seemed necessary to elevate our activities above the exercise of amateurs would define my experience as coach.

To evade Coach's looming shadow I added my own layer of insight to the dialogue, describing the conceit for today's session as informed by the desire to experience a connection between the now detached vegetation areas of Fletchers Gully where we stood, and the park, which was the site of the proposed stair-sprint session. I wanted to suggest I'd created this route in part as a continuation of a theme to do with the forgotten connectedness of landscapes, but I resisted appearing too deliberate and instead reminded Morgan to let the rhythm of the landscape dictate the pace rather than going out too hard.

Morgan still started out too fast for my liking, so I yelled out a reminder: It's important that the run feels as effortless as possible in these early stages, otherwise your running spirit might retreat into its shell. He responded diligently and cut back the pace so we ran together.

Unfortunately a game of cricket was being played on Waverley Oval, so we were forced to content ourselves solely with a session of stair sprints. It was eleven o'clock by this stage and already quite hot, with the usual small patch of sweat darkening the blue cloth of my t-shirt right in the centre of my chest and crescents of sweat beginning to edge their way along the edges of Morgan's singlet. I felt the much-desired spring arrive in my step as we followed the path through the grove of pine trees that formed a barrier on the eastern side of the slope, and began to develop some high hopes for the session.

Before the first repetition we stopped to admire the sense of symmetry expressed by the stairs which led directly to the centre of the large circular water reservoir on top of the hill. Its playful peach-and-cream colouring contrasted with its authoritative position at the peak of the hill. It looks like a tomb, Morgan suggested, and

I agreed that the atmosphere of the place seemed oddly energised by some non-living agency. Fortunate to our plans, there was a bubbler placed not far from the base of the steps and some patchy shade provided by the pines.

I suggested we belt out each rep close to our maximum capacity. Morgan took this as an invitation to really flog himself and I couldn't resist trying to apply myself with the same level of ferocity. Despite feeling breezy for the first four repetitions and very much enjoying myself, I soon began to experience heat duress. Without thinking about it too much I found myself sneaking off to the shade between each repetition and walking in aimless spirals, tipping large quantities of water on my face and in my hair, grabbing the branch of a nearby tree and swinging my chest forward so my arms took my weight, opening up my chest and relieving my legs for a short while. Talking in such a state was impossible, beyond the occasional expletive about the difficulty of the situation. My entire being was mustered in minimising and enduring the impact of the heat. Any respite, no matter how miserly, seemed worthwhile: an extra second or two in the shade, running with a wet hat, a trip to the tap to refill our bottles and soak our heads.

Standing at the tap after the eighth repetition I felt such a deep physical need for water, and gratitude at its presence, that it seemed almost to assume the nature of a being to whom I might offer thanks or on whose care I depended not just for physical but even emotional nourishment. My experience was informed by a binding sense of camaraderie with Morgan, who had like me chosen to undergo the test forced upon us by the heat.

We waited at the base of the steps a little longer before the ninth rep, and two shirtless men joined us after leaving their bikes in the shade. Both had military-style haircuts, camouflage shorts and delicate silver necklaces. They immediately began ascending the stairs in a series of unique hopping movements, the slimmer of the two showing superior ability. They were completing their second repetition as Morgan and I descended from our ninth. I encouraged them with a thumbs-up gesture and one responded with a muffled 'Is good' in an accent I stereotyped as Russian.

Morgan and I agreed that we were glad to have some company and we completed the final three reps with the kind of dedication difficult to manufacture without an audience. At the conclusion of the twelfth repetition we could do nothing more than throw ourselves on the ground under the tree and pour water on our faces. I looked across to Morgan, whose chest was heaving up and down, arms stretched back behind his head, stroking and patting the lower trunk of the tree in the kind of undirected but entirely efficient manner necessary to incorporate that branched being into our elaborations of stress and relief.

After an extended recovery and further dousing of ourselves we decided to make our way back to the beach. The first stop was a closer inspection of the peculiar plateau upon which the water reservoir stood. This meant making our way up the stairs yet again, this time very slowly. The Russians were still punishing themselves with unconventional routines, sometimes leaping as many as four or five steps at once on one leg. Morgan and I called out numerous encouragements in our post-exertional bliss.

The plateau featured a bizarre confluence of elements, including the remnants of a circular sandstone structure beneath the turf that resembled a set of worn-down molars. Like the vaguely radial forms employed in the arrangement of the houses and internal reserves in Killara, this barely visible circle of sandstone blocks seemed to express some ancient purpose, and I felt a weak though agreeable desire to perform some ritual gesture involving water to manifest my feelings to Morgan.

Three, maybe four structures that looked like orphaned gateposts were scattered over the hilltop, conforming to the same jaunty colour scheme as the larger above-ground reservoir. On closer inspection I could see their decorative tops were made from a steel-latticed screen, which led me to conclude they were vents for the structures below the ground. Like the circle of sandstone, these apparently choreographed particulars left me feeling as though I'd wandered into some kind of charged performative zone, the exact powers of which were invisible to my consciousness while successfully going to work in subtle though profound ways on my inner being.

In addition to the vent posts, the large above-ground reservoir was accompanied by what looked to be an antechamber of some sort, again in peach and cream and complete with the same recessed, curved archways cut into its walls, featuring decorative pilasters, cornices and parapets. This structure took a rectangular form and was much smaller.

Morgan and I stood by one of the vents at the far edge of the plateau looking south-east across the pine grove and the playing fields below to the strip of ocean and the horizon blurred in the distance. We were both sweating profusely. Morgan removed his hat, wiped his brow and, before returning it to his head, splashed the inside with water from his bottle. I've never been up here, he said, and his voice suggested a feeling I shared, that the discovery of such a strange place makes you feel as though it has been calling you for some time.

As we took a steady route down the slope, I was sure to exclaim once or twice on the quality of the sandy turf and my delight at seeing the beds of orange-brown pine needles on the floor of the grove.

When we hit a perfectly rectangular pitch with bright, almost blindingly white gravel cut into the grass, I wondered whether I'd be able to cope with any more perplexing and commendable pieces of public infrastructure. Morgan said it was a bocce or boules pitch, since bowls is on grass, and that the two hefty wooden sleepers at either end functioned as buffers for the stray balls. It was hard to imagine it getting much use, nestled away down the back side of the park, but I enjoyed the idea of an entire community of users lurked somewhere in the surrounding dwellings, deeply committed to their esoteric vocation. The flat, white surface vibrated with potential and I conceived a game of cricket that might be held there at some point in the future. Morgan was pressing his fingers into his neck, no doubt to gauge the seriousness of a pimple. I looked back up to the hill we'd jogged down and again at the pitch, attempting to hold together in my head the eccentric elements that littered this park, which until now had remained anonymous to me.

We continued along a path past the high concrete wall of another reservoir, much larger than the others, so large it was difficult to get an idea of exactly how big it was. All these structures must be capitalising on the gravity afforded by the hilltop, I said to Morgan, resisting the temptation to stretch an analogy to the religious buildings of the Kensington peak, which were similarly gathered there for a less substantial but perhaps no less efficacious sense of gravity.

We followed Birrell Street back down to Bronte Beach and plunged our sizzling bodies into the water before sheltering under the rock face to cool down further and to elaborate plans for our next session. I noticed the two Russian men we'd met on the stairs doing some stretches in the soft sand. They were writhing around on their backs, battering themselves in sand. After arching and contorting their bodies both men rose and walked towards the breakers. They expressed an infectious sense of conviviality and I found myself resisting a desire to jokingly ruffle Morgan's hair, throw a few dummy punches into his ribs or tackle him into the sand and raise both my arms in the air, shouting: Roman victor! Instead we stood there quietly in the damp, quickly fading cool of the rock ledge looking out at the near-catastrophic brightness of sun, sand and water.

I thought about the trials of adolescence and wondered whether the basic forms of my own difficulties during that period were being recreated through different content inside Morgan's steadily churning mind: feelings of impotence, frustration, destructive yearning, awkwardness concerning a sense of personal style or character. I wondered whether Alex had to accommodate the splitting of self that the genetic misfortune of something like acne often provokes during adolescence, whether her seeming invulnerability and self-assuredness was due to overcoming prior trials of this kind, or to the luck of never having had to face them in the first place. I wondered whether, like me, Morgan had retreated to an inner world during adolescence: the pain of self-awareness and uncontrollable bodily transformations demanding the elaboration of what Coach had described as an immunity-granting inner mythology. I looked at Morgan's peculiar hat and thought about the various hopes I had for items of clothing that would either allow me to hide or transcend my present identity.

The Russian men returned, picked up their belongings and walked along the sand, back towards the gully. I pointed to them as they walked away, shoulders knocking occasionally. Morgan squinted under the brim of his hat and took a long slug of water from his bottle.

Castlecrag

The pretext for our Castlecrag run was a set of stair sprints, even though I was yet to complete a reconnaissance mission to see whether an adequate set of stairs for our purposes existed in the suburb. When broaching the idea with Morgan on our prior run, he let on that he knew a little of the area because his uncle and aunt had for a number of years rented a house there. As a result he also knew that its original master planners were Walter Burley

Griffin and Marion Mahony Griffin, the designers of the nation's capital, though it was hard to say whether this detail provided him the same excitement as such knowledge brought me. The mention of a further set of blood relatives, my speculation as to the extent to which they were different from and similar to Alex, and the shred of interest expressed by Morgan in architectural history, all combined to buoy my spirits to such a degree that even after a gruelling day of window-washing in the heat I was compelled to exhaust my energies with the challenge of completing one hundred burpees in under seven minutes.

My excitement was further intensified by what I read online about the suburb later that day. I discovered Castlecrag was meant to be an exemplary if not entirely viable realisation of a garden suburb, where the built environment worked in harmony with nature rather than against it. The fifteen Griffin houses in the suburb were sculpted from local sandstone and sat unobtrusively in the landscape. The aesthetic principles the Griffins had imagined would long govern the feel of the place had not always been sympathetically observed, but the general consensus was that Castlecrag was a distinctive suburb deserving of mention in any catalogue of visionary architecture and planning.

We began our tour on Edinburgh Road. I hoped that in our travels we would find an appropriate set of stairs for our training session. Morgan wore the same black wide-brimmed hat, large glasses and a decent coat of tinted sunscreen that I took to be in part sun protection and in part an effort to obscure his skin for cosmetic reasons. He had two nectarines from a tree in his yard, and he insisted I try one immediately. As I ate, he observed, awaiting a response. The nectarines were unlike any I'd sunk my teeth into that summer. They weren't floury like the kind refrigerated for lengthy periods, nor overly sinuous and juicy. Instead the flesh fell off the seed, with the abundant juiciness retained largely within the rich yellow pulp. They had a sharp, floral fragrance which moved me to imagine the bare slope where a nectarine tree grew on my family's farm, the foreground dotted by occasional fringes of blond grass and a few scattered limestone rocks, and in the background a row of ironbarks along a barbed-wire fence. As I ate I imagined there was something in the relationship between this setting, the nectarine I was eating, and Morgan, Alex and their extended family, which all contributed to what I felt to be the best experience of eating stone fruit, perhaps any fruit, in my life, providing optimal hydration before a taxing session in the hottest point of a summer day and at the same time healing the damage to my soul.

From Edinburgh Road we followed a small laneway up over the rise of the hill. The road thinned to a footpath that threaded through bushland at the back of various houses. Occasionally we'd glimpse views across to neighbouring hillsides in Middle Harbour, before the path would turn us back into a small portion of bush or a bulging lump of the sandstone escarpment that seemed as much a feature of the landscape as any human dwelling.

We emerged from the bush to meet with another road, taking a left down to a small roundabout from which a thick stand of native scrub, featuring banksia, casuarina, wattle, grevillea and small eucalyptus, had sprung. Morgan led the way around to the other side of the roundabout and we plunged again into the bush, this time down a steeper, narrower path to meet with a lower layer of vegetation: floppy-leafed palms, grasses and ferns.

The path continued along the side of the steeply sloping hillside, occasionally opening out into landscaped areas where the wet sandstone showed through the vegetation, and rustic steps cut out of rock led the way.

This is entirely unique, I said to Morgan, who had now removed his sandals and was picking a drier route through the undergrowth with his bare feet.

The path emerged from the bushland and stuck close to the fence line, which bordered the sometimes unassuming, sometimes grand backyards of the houses below. One house was an almost classic realisation of the vernacular red-brick terracotta-roofed suburban type, complete with Hills hoist and wedge of couch grass. We peered around to see the extent of the thing stretching forward to the street front. It revealed a massive multistorey construction supported by concrete pillars as the slope dropped away. The tip of the iceberg, I said, thinking of the time I saw my pulled wisdom teeth.

Aside from one woman washing her dog, the yards were largely empty, though we often heard the excited yells of children some way off down the slope.

Prior to the walk I'd been working out ways to offer Morgan advice on his skin condition. I suffered from a mild case of seborrhoeic dermatitis that tended to flare up in response to stress, and I decided a discussion of my trials managing this condition might help normalise the feelings of disappointment and shame which I assumed characterised Morgan's experience of acne. My speculations about whether my observing these imperfections somehow evened the ledger between Alex and me were deactivated by a feeling of sympathy, and the instinct that shared knowledge of my own difficulties would have greater redemptive power.

I pulled out my little flask of apple cider vinegar in a deliberately conspicuous fashion when we sat to rest on a rock, and as was my habit applied this liberally to the regions of my face punctuated by hair follicles and across the bridge of my nose where the dermatitis outbreaks usually occurred. Despite the conspicuousness of my actions, Morgan remained silent, tapping a stick he'd picked up on a rock in front of us as though sounding out its core.

Cutting my losses I began: I have always had a deep affection for apple cider vinegar, since it rescued me from a period of persistent anguish. I held the bottle out to Morgan and shifted it to a patch where the sunlight cut through the canopy to illuminate the browny-orange liquid inside. After I returned from my overseas travels I shaved off my beard to find a virulent network of rash, with red skin fringed by dried flakes spreading across my chin and underneath my jaw. I identified this as the same condition that had previously been limited to my eyebrows and scalp. It seemed to worsen after hot drinks, dry weather, alcohol and stress. My window-washing job left me in the unfortunate position of being able throughout the day to catch my face in a reflective surface and inspect it more or less continuously, so the presence of the rash came more and more to saturate every element of my consciousness.

I had tried a number of solutions, I continued to Morgan, fish-oil supplements advised by a naturopath, letting dandruff shampoo dry for long periods on my face before washing it off, applying abundant quantities of moisturiser, various mild steroids and other useless ointments in metal tubes offered by overpaid, insensitive dermatologists. Not to mention a solution of olive oil and honey that made me particularly attractive to flies. My brother had begun to suffer from a similar condition at around the same time, which led him to investigations on the internet for possible remedies. Apple cider vinegar was one of the potential solutions he unearthed, and its efficacy was striking. With careful management my outbreaks are now kept to a minimum.

I was happy with the elaboration of my anecdote, despite Morgan not responding and continuing to tap the rock. I speculated hopefully that a silent bond was building between us, supported by shared experiences of skin affliction, exercise routines and a growing interest in space and aesthetics, in particular our shared appreciation of public green spaces in suburbs.

We continued on through the last of the forest and up a set of stairs that though smaller than I'd hoped appeared to be the closest thing to an adequate setting for our training session. I didn't mention this to Morgan, in the hope we would find a larger set later on our tour.

Morgan led us to yet another hidden walkway which trailed up between two Griffin-designed houses that appeared at once unimposing, in the sense that their low roofs and sandstone walls made them seem like bunkers formed out of the materials common to the site, and assertive, with the thick sandstone shaped into peculiar, vaguely threatening crystalline forms. The path functioned as a viewing platform, twisting and turning between houses, strips of bush and rock outcrop. It fed around the side of one of the houses, offering a relatively direct view of its backyard and of a bulging three-peaked ornament like a tiara suspended above the back door. Morgan and I agreed the contrasting effects of the Griffin designs seemed appropriate to the gnarled, spiky, bulbous, sinuous and spiny harmony of the surrounding vegetation.

The path transitioned into a driveway before becoming a path again, which then led to a reserve which appeared to be the highest in the suburb. Unlike the other reserves, here two tennis courts were built in the centre, in one of which a man and boy were engaged in a tennis match. We found a tap that formed part of the steel piping in the tennis court fence and refilled our bottles, admiring that it functioned as a system for the distribution of water and a fence at the same time.

We sat on the bench for a while drinking under our hats. I couldn't resist offering an aside to Morgan about how I found tennis courts a source of great romance, and suggested we should one day visit Woollahra Library to appreciate the vantage out over the fenceless, grassy court at *Elaine*. Tennis courts also had a privileged spot in his own past, Morgan said, due to an oath he'd pledged on the periphery of one with a girl he had liked who wore the coolest sunglasses he'd ever seen. They'd conduct mock battles with plane-tree seedpods and he'd have cordial at her house afterwards.

This more or less perfect scene took shape and faded into the static throb of cicadas and the regular volleys of the two tennis players. We both looked ahead at the game and the fringes of bush at the edges of the court.

I saw there were two spare racquets that the duo must have brought with them leaning against the side of the fence, and tentatively suggested to Morgan that instead of our run today we propose a game of doubles. He looked at me with raised eyebrows, an expression that reminded me of Alex, the likely meaning of which I ignored and, thinking of the better side to Coach Fitz, called out to the pair to ask whether they'd be interested in a game. Yah, said the man, sure. I'm Guy, this is my son Jonty. I introduced myself and Morgan. We don't have racquets, I said, would you mind if we borrowed? Yah, no problems, one of you will have to make do with that small one. Do you also mind if I also borrow some sunscreen, I said? Yah, sure, said Guy, coming over to the fence to introduce himself formally. We're on a tour of the suburb, I told him. You don't live here, do you? he said. A tour, what kind of tour? An architectural tour, I said, we're interested in the Griffins and the history of the garden suburb. Are you residents? Yah, said Guy, I've heard of this Griffin, we aren't in one of his houses though. It must be fantastic living in a place that seems as much designed for the foot-traveller as the car, I said. It makes me think how the convenience required for cars has locked off so many other affordances and moods offered by the landscape. I saw Guy's eyes begin to glaze over and knew from past experiences in which I had spent too much energy explaining my activities to uninitiated randoms that it would be best if I quickly put a halt to any emotional labour I was planning to invest in the exchange and instead direct my ambitions towards the game of tennis. Us versus you, I suggested? Sure, said Guy, before yelling at Jonty: *Come meet the tourists.*

Morgan was a far better player than I'd imagined and the game took shape around a steadily increasing competitiveness between him and Guy, who twice smashed forehands into the back of his son and blamed him for not getting out of the way. I made an effort to set a contrasting example and stifled my typical urges to blame contingencies or abuse my racquet, instead moving diligently between points in a manner I hoped was reminiscent of Andre Agassi. We played out two sets, winning one a piece, before Guy and Jonty had to go. We shook hands across the net in the customary fashion and handed back the kit.

Not quite feeling we'd completed enough of a session, I suggested we do a few strides up and down the court, the benefits of which I outlined to Morgan, who nodded with dazed but seemingly not indifferent agreement. We strode along in unison down opposite sides of the court, knocking out fifteen repetitions. Afterwards we more or less showered ourselves under the tap in the fence and sheltered for a while in the shade, where I attempted to finish the discourse I'd begun in the presence of Guy. I love how the materials for the Griffin houses are a perfect fit for the surrounding bush, which seems a combination of the threatening and the soft. Morgan had adopted his customary gesture of tapping the ground, this time with a small sandstone rock he'd picked up. How would you feel about completing a small writing task on the place, I said. Nothing major, just a few sentences, and I'll do the same? Sure, said Morgan, dropping the rock, sure. I hoped my boldness in requesting the game of tennis hadn't produced the same trepidation that Coach's antics had inspired in me. But I figured there was a point at which the desire to avoid any association with Coach Fitz might in itself become a maladaptive goal to which I could become enthralled. I reassured Morgan that we would make up for the absence of stair sprints in our next session, thanked him for the nectarine and asked whether he needed a lift anywhere. I might retrace our steps for the writing task, and then get Dad to come get me, he said, a response that provoked further speculation about how I could arrange a meeting with more members of the family.

Morgan Opens Up

After our next morning run in Centennial Park Morgan suggested we stop for a quick coffee in the café there. He insisted on taking a short detour past a large, sinewy Moreton Bay fig with particularly cavernous buttress roots. When we got to the tree Morgan reached his hand up into one of the recesses in the truck and pulled out a small, slightly roughed-up black leather book. He made no reference to it at all and we continued on to the café.

Morgan ordered an apple crumble and a black coffee with milk on the side, and I had a flat white with a slice of banana bread. I made an effort to ensure I was particularly friendly, perhaps even to the degree of subservience, when engaging with the waitstaff, due to my paranoia that I show any resemblance to Coach Fitz.

We perched ourselves on the bar stools at the ledge window next to a stack of old magazines, which Morgan kept leafing through distractedly. For some reason I found this oddly unsettling and I felt compelled to change the ambience between us by engaging him in some kind of game. I began to read out the headlines, hoping to relax us both: 'The End: Nicole's Heartache Over Claims Keith Has Secrets', 'Double Joy', 'The Miracle Baby Healing My Heart', 'Grecian Heights', 'Wild Pets', 'Yes, We're in Love Again', 'The New Food Revolution'. It feels like we're in the bow of a ship, said Morgan, rocking back on his stool. There'll be fog on the shore tonight, boatswain, I said, adopting an antiquated intonation and saluting the view from our perch.

Together we looked out over the park, where the characteristic mixture of kinetic activity settled the mood somewhat. A gust of wind caught one of the newspapers and I leapt up from my seat to chase it out into the park. When I returned I saw that Morgan had left his diary on the bench in front of my seat. I looked at him and wondered whether he looked more like his mother or father, both of whom were coming to occupy increasingly large places in my imaginings, despite having no clear and distinct visual information regarding their appearance. I tried to convey to Morgan that I had seen the journal but remained unsure of what it was or what to do with it. As I was about to ask, he said, Okay, sorry, look, I've got to go. You can have my food. Sorry, but let's run again next week. He picked up his hat, pulled it down hard over his head, and began his jog home while still in the café.

I sat there in his absence, mind racing due to the double dose of caffeine, and imagined myself at once an important and yet still illegitimate consul adopted by the family. I picked up Morgan's journal and gauged its weight in my hand. I felt I needed to be in its presence for a while before I could open it up.

At the Farm

In late January every year I observed the tradition of returning to my family's farm in the central west of New South Wales. I had two weeks before school went back and the window-washing season began. During that time of year my mum's vegetable patch was particularly fecund, producing an almost burdensome harvest of tomatoes, cucumbers, zucchinis and melons, while in the orchard figs, grapes, and white and yellow peaches were usually in abundance. I was sure to live out the image that I had nurtured in my mind throughout the year, of picking a warm peach or fig from the tree and eating it in the sunshine. This extended period of feasting and recollection would, I hoped, restore any mineral and emotional resources that may have been taxed while I went about my activities in the city.

Next to me in the car while I drove to the farm was Morgan's black diary, an item of greater promise than the *Best Bets* or Tuesday's Good Living liftout. I had vague but unshakeable intentions about the appropriate atmospheric conditions for reading the book and decided there would be no better place than the bedroom in my family home, a place where I had undergone my own inner battles with the way I imagined myself to appear to others, and with what I felt I needed to do to alter and transcend such conceptions. I speculated about whether it would contain similar prose to that in my own adolescent journals, which, upon reviewing them in later years, seemed typified by the pervasive sense both of anxiety and hope, and I wondered about the extent to which Morgan's writing would allow me to melancholically reinhabit my time with Alex or, by contrast, whether it would offer an unforeseen perspective on the world, mediated through language.

As well as taking Morgan's journal with me, this trip would be different due to my new and more expansive approach to distance running. Where previously my runs on the farm were confined to a nine-kilometre track known as the laneway circuit, now, due to my hunger for kilometres, I would need to run the same route repeatedly, seek out additions to the existing circuit, or create an entirely new route.

I left Sydney very early so I would beat peak-hour traffic and drive with the sun at my back. The route through the Blue Mountains typically involved a short pit stop in Blackheath where I would refuel with a treat from a bakery I liked and a strong coffee.

Blackheath was a cold and miserable little island of winter, despite Sydney being muggy and hot when I left. I spent some time leafing through a Good Living I'd saved from late last year to tide me over during the summer months, when an inadequate holiday feature replaced it. Durack was in Bondi, mincing it up in a new Italian-Japanese-Nordic fusion restaurant. It was one of his better reviews. A nice through-line in the piece created a sense of humour and coherence. Sadly, the Kitchen Spy section was missing – it seemed to be less of a regular feature these days – but Richard Cornish was still responding to 'vexing culinary questions' in his informative, often funny column, and Huon Hooke identified various wines in bottle shops around the city, some of which I hoped to locate on my return. The Bargain of the Week, identified as being for sale in the Summer Hill Wine Shop, looked well within my grasp. Perhaps in the near future I would go there to buy it for a picnic on a grassy slope overlooking part of the harbour or a beach. I would pair the wine with some sharp yet creamy, complex-smelling cheese, grassy olive oil and moist, fluffy bread.

The heat and blue sky returned as I descended the mountains to Lithgow, then to Bathurst and Orange. The grass this year was longer and despite the dry weather seemingly more robust than in recent summers. Water had pooled to form light-catching dams in hollows that typically remained hidden. I pulled over at a service station just outside Bathurst to refuel, and endured an internal debate over whether I should get cola and chips to really make it feel like a road trip. My concession to the temptation was a mineral water and mixed nuts which I'd almost finished before pulling out onto the highway.

As I entered the home stretch of my trip from Orange to Molong, I fished out a CD from deep within the glove box of the Odyssey, a greasy, smudged, heavily scratched thing marked with my own scrawled hand: *CD God put in my car to remind me of the embarrassments of my youth*. I had a rough idea of the track list and after persisting through some of the skipping in the earlier songs, settled on the soundtrack to *Gladiator*, which immediately stirred a series of composite yet seamlessly interwoven visions sculpted in part from the movie, in part from my own re-imaginings of the movie as a youth, and the adaptation of those older imaginings to my current emotional states. The important parts of the scene were a field of blond grass of roughly waist height, and a hand, my hand, brushing through this grass: there was a party coming up, a party on the horizon, and my wanderings were in some nearby but connected time or space. I remembered the other times I'd driven this route, either returning home filled with romantic possibilities freshly scraped from late evenings with friends and night wanderers, or travelling in the other direction, on my return to Sydney, restored and with certain visions nurtured to such a degree that they no longer resembled anything that would mesh with the reality that awaited me in the city.

The process of arriving at my family home followed a rhythm of intricate sensory triggers and reassurances. There was the slowing of the car along the drive and my apprehensive inspection from a distance of the garden, a landmark of clustered green amid the dry paddocks. I felt the shudder of the vehicle as it crossed the cattle ramp and the gentle sweep of the road as it curved past the carob bushes and deodars, where I'd constructed elaborate cubby houses as a child, where piles of limestone rocks lay to denote the graves of dead sheepdogs and where I'd hidden precious bottles of stolen beer in the dirt to drink with high school friends on moonlit walks through the paddocks. As the vehicle rounded the final bend, I would look to see if any dogs had been alerted by the sound of the vehicle, in which case they would appear, at first concerned, then excited by the presence of familiar company.

I parked the car and as soon as I opened the door our pet labrador Larras flooded the interior with his exuberance. I made a knowingly feeble attempt to placate him as I collected my various possessions from the vehicle and entered the house through the creaking flyscreen door. It wasn't until I left home that its smell had become explicit to me, like an elusive signature as immersive and emotional in its impact as a favoured song.

I shed my shoes and bags before entering the relative cool and dark of the kitchen, where Mum and Dad were waiting at the table to greet me. We chatted about the length of the journey, traffic in certain segments, weather transitions and pit stops. After tea and cake, my mum told me I was like a cat on a hot tin roof, unable to sit still and eat, preferring to repeatedly inspect the contents of fridge and pantry as I had done since my adolescent days. I knew a dose of vigorous exercise with my favourite 'squat rock' down on the tennis court would be required to settle my restlessness. I put the finishing touches on the unpacking process, changed into lighter clothes and made my way down to the far corner of the yard, to the entrance of the court, enjoying the gentle pop of scattered acorns in the lawn under my feet.

The tennis court had been a multipurpose recreational space throughout my growing up. Its flat, hard surface provided the rare predictability required to generate equitability in ball games like cricket, tennis and basketball. Years of neglect had done little to reduce the performative energy of the place. Although the clay surface was now scabbed over with dark mosses, stray dents and tufts of weed, I still experienced a sense of occasion as I surveyed the open, level space. My rock lay in a shaded area off to the side of the court. A large limestone lump I'd poached from a stack Dad had collected from the paddocks and stowed near the house for his various projects building dry-stone walls and paths. Its surface had been warmed by the sun and as I turned it over with a foot, spiders and ants scurried for cover among cracks and nearby leaves. When I picked it up and clutched it to my chest the heat was just on the verge of burning and its rougher parts grazed the softer skin underneath my arms. I used the horizontal wires in the fence as a line of sight and began the first of four circuits built around squats, with the rock as the key fatigue-inducing element.

At the end of the session I lay on the ground and followed the veining of the oak tree branches that extended out over the court. I reflected on my studious efforts over the years perfecting the accuracy of various projectiles or channelling blood flow to particular muscles so my body took the form I desired. I found the time to subject my body to the rigours of push-ups, chin-ups and abdominal exercises even on days when farm work extended from dawn to dusk and when the cold, wet winter evenings gave the warm fire in the lounge room immense appeal. The exercises had become an end in themselves, but an end which built resilience and allowed me to experience for the first time the delights of outdoor gyms, and to flex with a sense of pride and restrained grace like a large cat might in the sun before a hunt on the savannah.

The night of my return my mum made a salad filled with zesty dark-green leaves, some of which were hardy and rough enough to graze my tongue, others soft and fat, things that exuded a silky, clear sap when they tore; others made a crunching sound so loud it was difficult eat without being self-conscious. All of it was delicious. This was paired with a generous helping of chilli-and-garlic pasta I made with oily, fragrant garlic, early-season tomatoes, generous glugs of olive oil, shaved parmesan, herbs and fresh chillies. We retold shared stories about visitors finding slugs in their salad, the time my paternal grandfather happily ate a maggot-riddled peach, and the slippery, moist shock of a banjo frog nestled underground that Mum experienced when digging potatoes. Then came stories about the dogs, an entire archive of memories about our lives with these beings, both clearly recollected and vague, in tones of nostalgia and amusement. Stories of dogs eating socks, entire flocks of chickens, of the dogs who were best for the paddock and best for the yard, of the progress of young dogs, of lazy, stubborn and disobedient dogs, of brave, tireless and greedy dogs, of Dad's catastrophic failure at the sheepdog trials, of Jack, Blister, Spark, Coke, Tup, Hellie, Cyril, Frank, Patch, Larras, Slim, Percy, Pikelet, Noodle, Monty, Zac, and how their lives measured our own.

After washing up I spent close to an hour on my back in the sunroom looking at the ceiling fan while Mum and Dad watched a picturesque murder mystery on the television. I took a cup of tea to my bedroom on the other side of the house and prepared an environment appropriate for focused reading, lighting a few candles, getting into comfortable clothes, and ensuring my phone was beyond reach.

There was still a little light left outside. I could hear a sprinkler and the ricocheting sounds of crickets and frogs around the garden.

I began reading. In addition to making sense of the content, my mind worked to assess the particular qualities of the writing. While resoundingly peculiar, unlike in my own cringe-worthy adolescent writing there was little to be embarrassed about in Morgan's journal. A combination of mild trepidation at my own comparatively limited intellectual abilities and a deeper sense of pride at having a subject of such quality were the dominant feelings that coloured my experience of reading.

Sometimes I was convinced the prose was exemplary of a stereotypical late-adolescent mind. However, after lulling me into a sense of knowing, it would offer a profound surprise, some insight of magnitude or flexing of the imagination that made me question the powers of my own mind.

Often the entries would begin by tracing over a piece of mundane information, about the weather or a daily event for instance, which would then be immediately shattered and rearranged by the use of a peculiar metaphor: 'Why did it nearly bring me to tears when I heard how a seventeen-year-old boy punched out a man for pushing his father through glass? It's not something I'd expect myself to be emotional about. But that's it, we can't second-guess the directions of our feelings accurately, and when we do it's a very lukewarm form of achievement, decomplicating oneself, kind of like buying a meal and heating it up.'

I composed my own lines of review in response to Morgan's entries, noting that his writing featured sporadic efforts to sabotage the banal with imaginative exuberance, bathos, whimsy and random fictionalisation. I told him that what sometimes seemed like the awkward, hopped-up, pop-philosophical acrobatics of an undergraduate morphed into third-person perspectives on scenes that evolved a new way of looking at things. I would be sure to provide an example: 'A day of patchy winds and white grease-stained paper bags. A group of sparrows have just descended on the elm and I immediately thought of the fungi I had been thinking about earlier. Just as a piano key is struck, the china cups are collected and the breakfast things are put away, it is now time for lunch, or will be after a short break, where we might discuss things such as relationship status, dirty laundry, group politics, etc. Women walk across the square, a child waves his red sleeve and from above we see water burst from the fountain. I restore my gloves and continue to scratch the arch of my foot, it's white like wet meat on a rock. It felt like rain all day but the tables remain clear and dry. Why do I visit the exhibition so I can go to the bathroom? Why does my hand now feel like glass?'

Other entries tempted me to place the location: 'Slate gravestones, leaning pines, stone-fruit trees, zebra crossings, garden beds filled with pebbles, a red car, wooden window shutter, rust on white paint, the sound of the bus changing gears, an almost erotic type of empathy arises.' Meditations of this kind were interspersed with occasional quips of resounding insight, such as, 'Losing one sandal is as good as losing two,' 'So often it is a replenishing gesture to pretend you are crucified to the lawn,' or a particular observation that opened up a new way of regarding a familiar scene: 'Stop wearing my shorts, yells a man from his car. Kites hollow out invisible tubes in the air. The grass shakes. People carry chairs along the concrete path.'

Some entries featured an effort to plumb the depths of perceptual experience. For example, starting out by noting a blister on his lip and a perverse sense of contentment, Morgan would then confess how profoundly bored he was, 'so sick of the patterns of my mind', and then follow this internal observation of mood with a speculative account about the relationship between the potential and the actual, framed, as was often the case, by a meteorological observation: 'It's been a muggy day but the sun seems about to burst through the clouds. There is always an alternative on the horizon, or even just next to you, but the alternative never exists, it haunts our existence. What we come to remember as our existence is also an alternative, its privilege is only provisional. We sparkle with the pressure of near alternatives. Not to forget that our existence as it is, is no less privileged because of its provisional nature, and herein lies the difficulty.'

Here and there I would get the sense of romantic sentiments. However, these seemed to unearth fantasies that were at once eccentric and yet somehow more truthful than what is expressed in the familiar grinding of narrative. 'Just another day. Drizzle during what I saw of the morning, then, after a massive shopping trip, sun! Have found a nice patch of grass to sit on and my gut is full of baguette. Oh, a little green bug has landed on my page and I've decided not to squash it. I live in the forest with people who think themselves ninjas, but I don't talk to them, to me they sound like a power drill. One day I will be having cordial under the elm tree with the woman of my dreams and I will think directly back to this moment as if it were a coin I'd happened upon in the grass. She will wear a tasselled cloak and give me chronic gut pains from laughter. She will like snacks and will be mature only to the extent that I'm comforted by her during sickness.' Or, 'So desperately do I want to follow boys around and dress them up as wizards, to see which ones look the best, see which ones dig their elbows into their sides as they sip on cocktails and scoff shoestring potato chips. Where is your wetsuit? one might say, to which I'd reply, I left it in the car park with my slippers.'

In addition to this youthful imaginative flair, Morgan would include laconic snapshots of closely observed detail, of public life and character as suggested by dress, posture and facial features, 'A light shower. A café courtyard. Broken pieces of glass wedged in bricks. Bent thatch fences. Old blonde woman.' Or, 'Man fixing camera, woman talking about holiday.' On other occasions these observations would be warped through subtle perspectival trickery, 'Man in a pink polo shirt attempts the listening test supported by a delicate hand. Meanwhile, a jealous onlooker is created.'

He seemed to have a deep sensitivity to the expressive possibility of forms, as though sometimes bodies and thoughts were characterised by a similar mutability and dynamism: 'When we detach our bodies wobble.' 'My face melts into a frown and then freezes. Waves play games with the shore.'

Among my favourite sections were a series of observations I couldn't help imagining took place at a campsite or on a holiday of some sort: 'Six more tins of tuna hidden behind the toy trains. We can't profit off it, seeing a fence-post glitch underwater in the credits. Cool ham on your dinner plate, jars of ketchup on the table.

Everybody comes in different shapes and sizes, some with dreadies n'stuff, some really smart guys. I'm already looking forward to the stories, Wednesday's carbonara on the front of my t-shirt, shoes filled with dust all over the mat, showers at odd times to get the best of the hot water. A half-full bottle of cordial is next to the tent. Tonight we'll do dinner early, it might be my last night here. I rub the balls of my feet on the coarse surface of a skateboard, think about tearing strips of cloth from a sheet and draping it over a brown collarbone. Where is the mustard? Wind in the bamboo makes everybody's teeth appear white.'

Much of the writing was animated by a desire and a sense of play, as though Morgan were scrupulously observing the way his body and the environment became the material for feelings: 'The question is of where, at certain moments, my desire is directed: not directly at you, not quite at what it is you lie on either, but at both. At the chipped white and grey stones that are scattered underneath your chest and your elbows, at the cold leaking clouds, at the melted plastic on which you rest your skull. A blue triangular flag points to nowhere, someone's voice arrives slowly but loudly as if it were edging its way out of a packet. The tips of my fingers taste sour. I've been cutting lemon and rubbing chicken with lemon and oil. There is a square with another square cut from its middle. It's a table and we all sit around it with our hats on. I take an ant from my finger and throw it to the clay surface of the tennis court. We each take a sip from our glasses at the same time and agree that we must stay here in the corner, underneath the shade of the oak tree. Gumnuts crackle under our feet as we shift them with excitement. A group between the bushes walks down a grassy slope, disappears, then traces the same path back upwards. Behind them blue sky brings the smell and taste of soggy chips and Sunday radio.'

I read Morgan's journal every night in the silence of my room, each night lifting it from its resting position on the old piano stool I used as a bedside table. I heard his voice bubble with exuberance, awkwardness and surprise. I amused myself copying out random fragments and letting them form scenes in my mind: 'Cold spirals of tomato pasta, half-eaten packets of corn chips, the folding and smoothing out of water. Stray arms of blackberry bushes, ornamental olive trees. Three men talk energetically beside me. I see myself disfigured in their eyes…A small woman in a pressed brown dress…I have once again found myself in a very close and perhaps restricting relationship with a park, feeling great about the word "tract"…Calm blocks of understanding. A coffee cup filled with orange peel.'

Certain parts provoked an irresistible forensic urge because they seemed more obviously autobiographical: 'As the diary reaches its closing stages I feel a pervasive sense of illness incorporated into all that I'm connected to. I feel wretched and parasitic, but at the same time extraordinary, decisive and vague. In short I feel nothing but contradictory impulses as though my moods were scanned into language.'

Each time Morgan tempted me to feel pity for him, some insight or sense that he had an excellent grip on his own feelings would reassure me that my worries were misplaced. In fact, reading his journal left me with a kind of ideal image, not unlike the one I had initially formed of Coach Fitz, but in this instance, perhaps because of the form through which the exchange of character had taken place, there was a sense of vulnerability built into my conception of his character that I felt confident would, paradoxically, make it more enduring.

I thought it unlikely that anyone else in Morgan's family had seen the journal, and became convinced that my role as a coach was to provide an additional modicum of security, so that the voice which became manifest in the writing would come into its own in the world. My feelings for Morgan were complicated by a growing sense of esteem and what I had started to admit to myself was a not entirely charitable curiosity, sustained from and hungering for more privileged information, greater access to his inner life and family.

Farm Run

After completing what I now saw as a relatively unambitious warm-up run on a Wednesday morning of around twelve kilometres, on the following Friday I decided to attempt a route I now called Pye's Track and Double Circuit, the combination of a new route (Pye's Track) and the doubling of the laneway circuit that had previously sated my desires for distance. In total the run would be around twenty-six kilometres.

On most days during summer on the farm, the period from six to eight in the early morning is the best time to run. At that stage of the day, a blanket of cool from the night still rests upon the paddocks, and the orange, yellow, purple and grey gravels that line the roads melt softly with the morning sky. At many stages of the run gauntlets of chatty birds perform their morning song and herds of curious young cattle bundle alongside before peeling off due to some unknown agency, tossing their heads and returning to the middle of the herd to seek out water or the shade of a tree.

The day I'd marked out for my longer run was overcast, relatively cool and threatening to rain. I delayed my starting time until much later than usual, around ten, and set off, placing a fig, two peaches and a bottle of water on a fence post near the homestead that I would pass after completing Pye's Track and the first of the two circuits.

Most of the run was on gravel roads, crossing private or public land. The first leg took me through the sparse hills near the farm, past an old quarry and a peculiarly shaped dam nestled in a valley on the land that once belonged to a man named Pye. Occasional groupings of foreign trees, such as quinces, figs and poplars, suggested some prior settlement or place of rest for drovers on horseback.

I hopped across a dry creek littered with saffron thistles and spinifex-like tufts of sharp grass that spiked my shins. I followed the creek down to the Bell River and took the tight road that fed between it and a steeply sloping hill, with the occasional sheer sandstone cliff to my left. This road led to a corrugated-iron pump house built by my grandfather. I recalled trips down to the river in my youth to observe Dad or my grandfather battling with the thing, a great, spluttering oily engine sitting a couple of metres below ground level, with violently spinning belts and nests of disturbed hornets and swallows usually making an escape or mounting an attack. Occasionally there'd be a snake coiled quietly among the pipes. The pump dragged water from the river to a couple of dams closer to our house, where another pair of pumps now sat distributing the water to other dams, troughs and tanks around the property.

At the pump house I used the stile made of bent metal piping to clear the barbed-wire fence, and met with the more regularly serviced gravel road for a steady climb back up the hill line leading down to the river, a stretch that from a vehicle had always struck me as perilous, and then carried onwards to the public road. It started to rain lightly and I felt refreshed. I observed the hazy curtains of rain and the different fronts of cloud making their way above the undulations of dampened blond straw and patches of clustered gums in the distance. The feeling of extreme openness and shifting dynamics of the landscape had a paradoxical effect of focusing my energies inwards.

I thought about cutting back up to the homestead for some supplies as I passed the driveway but as I felt reasonably spritely decided against it, and due to the cooling effect of the rain didn't imagine I was losing much fluid. It would be nine kilometres before I reached the fence post with my fruit and water, and with eight kilometres under my belt I guessed that I should be able to manage.

The rain became heavier on this stint of the run so I removed my floppy blue hat and wrapped it around my phone, which was already partially protected by the sheath of wetsuit material that I had used to fasten it to my upper arm. For the rest of the run I carried this increasingly wet package in my hand, continually speculating on whether the phone inside remained dry.

I crossed the still mostly dry Red Creek at the concrete crossing and followed the road through a flaking huddle of impressive yellow box eucalypts that bordered the road as it led up to the old railway crossing and onwards to the junction with Larras Lee Road. At the junction I took a right and continued along the gravel as it cut through a densely treed sandstone ridge, a place known as The Gap. On the other side of the ridge, the roadside verges transitioned into expansive paddock-like fields studded with dense tufts of grass, among them phalaris, kangaroo grass, and what looked to be a kind of sedge or rush. A few willows attended the banks of a steep but usually dry creek that cut through the open, fenceless stretch of roadside land, and wooden beehives in faded green, pink and yellow were scattered through a thick stand of yellow box trees on its far slope. As was often the case a small herd of cattle was grazing there, and as I passed they briefly abandoned their continual munching to move in parallel with me for a while.

The road climbed and then plateaued to an exposed stretch that I was glad to leave via a double gate back onto the private laneway that traversed our property. Here the road was less established, with much of the bare ground partially obscured by yellow burr and saffron thistle. I felt my spirits replenished as I was once again taken up into the land our family had grown accustomed to calling our own.

I recalled a snake I'd seen coiled near the cracked concrete crossing at the base of a dead yellow box tree and the time I'd collected the tips of several Bathurst burrs in my legs while I was sprinting along trying to set a record for the laneway circuit. These had busied me for as long as a month after I had returned to Sydney and taken up residence in a temporarily vacant room at the bottom level of a terrace where my brother lived. One burr in particular, just above my right knee, proved particularly stubborn and resisted many of my attempts to coax it out with pressure or pin. It gradually reddened to a hard, aching lump before I resorted to a blade from my window-washing kit that we used to scrape paint from the glass. Whether it was the sharpness of the blade or the burr's readiness to leave my flesh, it seemingly leapt out the moment I pressed the metal to my skin, surprising me in its length and leaving me with a deep sense of relief that I turned over and over in my mind for many days.

The thistle-strewn track zigzagged through another grouping of yellow box trees that marked out a dry gully and provided a sense of refuge in that otherwise bare expanse. The orange-brown clay of the track had become slick in the rain and I was forced to seek out the stable traction afforded by patches of grass running alongside the path, which made collision with a thistle more likely.

The gully represented the lowest point before the last climb up to the hill of Silo Stains, from where I would enjoy a steady downhill to my supplies perched on top of the post, which I had brought to mind often during the run and which I had begun to conceive of as a kind of sacrificial offering to the gods of athletics.

As I descended the hill a sudden and pronounced shift in the weather took place. The rain was hauled upwards into the fattening bright clouds, which spread to reveal decent tracts of blue sky, from which a hot sun beat down upon the wet clay.

A buzzing of insect life began, with each of my steps a fraught attempt to pick out a relatively unoccupied patch of earth amid an animated profusion of ants, moths, bees and wasps that were emerging onto the track.

I reached the fence post at the homestead, drained the small bottle of water I had there, ate a peach and a fig on the spot and carried the other peach with me in my pocket. Part of me felt a tug to go back inside for more water but the rain which had accompanied the better part of my run so far had lulled me into a false sense of security and I thought I'd manage the last nine kilometres, the second loop of the circuit, without needing further liquid. I imagined the inadequate substitute of sucking on the cloth of my rain-soaked hat or deviating from the track to lick the fronds of wattle bushes on the hill.

I unwrapped my phone and hooked my earphones into the base, selecting the playlist I'd been compiling specifically for the final stretches of a long run such as this. The effect of the music was immediate and intense. The pain from the aches in my muscles and the blisters on my toes faded out to nothing and for a while I continued on in a pellucid, weightless ambience as though my body had been dissolved in the sound. Buoyed by this change, I increased my speed for what must have been three kilometres before the music lost its efficacy and began to irritate me and I pressed stop. I was now left to complete the final six kilometres, from The Gap to home, in the heavy, hot air, without any water, utterly drained of enthusiasm and forced to conduct a continuing battle with a familiar voice tempting me to walk the last stretch.

The weight of the air, the sense that I was now carrying rather than being transported by a pain-ridden body, the increasing number of thistles embedded in my skin and the maddening amount of insect activity on the ground all combined to make me feel as though I was being harassed out of the landscape like some kind of encroaching villain.

I reached the house, fumbling desperately with gate latches, then shoelaces and clothes once I was inside. I stripped down to my underwear, fixed a large jug of lightly salted water and orange juice, and laid myself out on the carpet where my body seemed to function for a while like a fountain, sweat bubbling up through my skin and trickling in small rivulets down my sides.

Return of the Diary and a Story About a Dead Bird

Shortly after I returned to Sydney I met Morgan in Centennial Park, for a walk rather than a run. I took the unusual step of parking inside the grounds and met him at the corner of the raised playing fields near the underground water reservoir up on Oxford Street. It was twilight and the park a typical cacophony of parrot and bat sounds, the sky beginning to fill with winged creatures migrating against the pink and silver clouds to some secret festival in the direction of the horizon.

Morgan was waiting, facing west towards the sunset, still wearing his black broad-brim hat, fingers in the fence supporting his outstretched arms, hair catching the gusty but light breeze. I remembered Sarah Connor in a scene from *Terminator 2*, looking at a playground through a fence before everything burns due to a nuclear blast. Connor remained, shaking the fence even as the flesh burns from her body and she transforms into a skeleton.

I was harbouring this thought as I came up the grand old sandstone flight of stairs to the fields above where Morgan waited. I immediately realised that reading Morgan's journal would have a difficult to express but important influence on the way I perceived him. I had an urge to find a language that would allow me to speak in a way adequate to the writing in his journal. However, my attempts to recall the voice in the writing, and apply this to shared reference points in the landscape and our brief history together, was short-lived. As I handed over the journal I reverted to my preference for the prosaic, which, since reading Morgan's journal, I had increasingly come to see as mediating my relations with people and the manifestation of my character in their perception.

Was some of this written at a camp? I asked crudely. Some, he said. Some of it is very good, I said. Very alive. It's the kind of writing that captures how I felt once, though made strange by you. I wanted to add: I'm glad this shared knowledge of your past now exists as a binding force between us. Instead we looked in silence at the flows of birds and bats against the glowing sky. I imagined a soundtrack to our lives playing while the taller buildings in the distance towards Mascot exploded, vanishing into an abyss.

In a way that was barely apparent to me at the time, I substituted the urge to draw Morgan into an intimate dialogue through the shared language of his journal with the form of thought that seemed most immediately available to me: a training plan for the future. The next few months will involve some of our most intense periods of training, I said. First, we will increase the quantity of training and focus on strength, then we must aim to hone this fecund background into a foreground of increasingly high-quality training, before reducing the workload so our muscles can rest and rebuild before the race. Morgan nodded. The future is ours to conquer, he said, and I imagined the words carved into a wooden bench in the desert.

We walked together in the forest of Sydney blue gums just below the field, picking our way through the exposed roots, following a path selected randomly from the network of dirt trails. When we saw a willie wagtail pecking at the grass where the forest opened up to fields, Morgan mentioned that his dad, an avid birdwatcher, told him this species was in decline in the Sydney region and rarely seen in the north-eastern parts of the park anymore.

I observed the bird. It moved in exuberant puffs, swivelling and fanning its tail as though expelling a surplus of energy obtained from some unseen source. I decided to share a shameful story with Morgan, perhaps as a gesture of allegiance provoked by the sharing of the journal. For a period of what must have been two or so years, I began, I took to making slingshots from forked branches, squares of leather and rubber bands. I would usually seek out birds that had been identified as pests, such as sparrows and crows. On one of my missions I must have been feeling particularly belligerent and dispirited so that when I discovered a wagtail and its little spherical nest on a row of metal pipes out the back of the shed, I decided I could assuage my boredom by harassing it. I stood there at a sporting distance and must have fired twenty or more shots. More or less on autopilot, I would retrieve a stone from the ground at my feet, load it into the leather pouch and send the thing whizzing towards the increasingly agitated bird. I remember the details so clearly, I said to Morgan. I even remember the size and shape of the rock that would make the inevitable kill: a flatter stone that I would have rejected in more discriminating moments. The odd shape of the stone resulted in a shot that first swung out, away from the target, before curving back in to strike the bird on its side. It fell from its perch and spasmed in the dirt for a while before lying still.

I suspected Morgan might be taken aback by this admission of violence as we continued to watch the acrobatics of the live wagtail. I reassured him that the death of the bird was something like an apocalypse. As soon as I had made the transgression, everything changed. I was immediately confronted by a surge of regret and a pathetic, belated reverence for the bird. I took its dead body and buried it beneath a tree, marking the grave with a limestone rock and some of my own blood.

Have you killed any birds since, asked Morgan, to which I found myself having to lie because of one other, similarly shameful occasion in my later adolescence, when I killed a noisy miner which had got caught in a house using a hard-bristled wooden broom.

While we looped back up the gently sloping road to my car, I pondered the centrality of birds to my youth and my current experience of the city. They were everywhere, pervasive enough to become unimportant. They were a reliable enough presence to be something like pets and yet the transience and unpredictability that defined our relationships with them was something pet owners wouldn't tolerate. Imagine life without them, I said to Morgan, without their song and their endearingly persistent efforts to adapt to the peculiarities of the city.

I asked Morgan whether his dad would be interested in meeting to share some of his knowledge about birds. I'll ask, he said, before bidding me farewell at the base of the steps near where we'd met. Shall we hit the soft sands on Saturday and then complete our long runs on Sunday? I suggested. Morgan waved back in what I interpreted as agreement, and I wandered along the road above the blue gums to the Odyssey, planning out the week's training, trying to picture the face of Morgan's dad within Morgan and Alex, and wondering when I would see my next willie wagtail.

That night, when I returned to my room, I thought I ought to see what Alex was up to on Strava. Since reading Morgan's journal, and setting in motion the first steps to meet other members of Alex's family so as to observe their phenotypical relatedness and share in the general effervescence of their group behaviour, I had the lingering feeling my activity was likely to provoke curiosity, even concern, from her perspective. A trait of mine, of which I had only a distant inkling, was a certain obliviousness to distinctions between what was and wasn't appropriate in making social connections. While deep down I knew Alex would find my networking with her family perverse, I managed to convince myself that it was a natural thing to do and that she might even see it as endearing. In truth I was split by multiple contrasting sentiments: a vicarious urge to surround myself with prosthetic extensions that emerged from the desire of past romance and the romance of the past; an urge to realise my vocational ideal of coaching and improve Morgan's prospects as a runner and a human being; and one to continue the ongoing project of my own self-improvement by renewing bad memories with more positive, contemporary associations.

Alex had added a new run to her repertoire: a loop including the Regent's Park and Primrose Hill, two further locations which I reprimanded myself for not having visited during my time in the city. I imagined myself in London in the summer through a combination of references to landscape in a documentary about Amy Winehouse and my own limited memories of parks in the city. I wondered whether I should pre-empt Alex discovering my activities by writing her a short note, but decided this might be interpreted as a gesture consistent with perverse behaviour, and resolved to resist the temptation and wait until Alex inquired about her brother. Based on Morgan's verbal reticence with me, I thought it likely that Alex's curiosity in his training, should it exist, would have to be sustained by a diet of 'good', 'it's going well', and similar expressions.

Morgan's Dad and a Picnic at the Bronte Banksias

The plan for our Sunday morning run took the pleasingly predictable form of some repetitions of the Tamarama steps and running on the soft sand down at Bronte, followed by a picnic to meet Morgan's dad and celebrate the closing down of summer.

I jogged across from my parking spot at Tamarama to Iggy's bakery on Bronte Road, where the distinctive smell of milled grains baking wafted down the street. I splashed out and added a log of French butter and a wedge of parmesan to my order, complimenting the staff on the service they were offering to the city.

My Bronte days would be based either at the north or south end of the beach, depending on factors often not obvious to me. On south-side days I would lay out a towel on the small but steep grass slope, beneath one of the palm trees. From here I would make my forays into the water, choosing either the protected Bogey Hole if the swell was too messy, or the main part of the surf beach if the swell was more forgiving. On other days I would set up camp in one of the sheltered outdoor tables at the northern end. There were four tables to a shelter, each partitioned by weatherboard walls. I would lay out my goods on the table, depending on the winds and what was available, and eat breakfast or lunch with a vantage out over the beach and the ocean beyond.

After jogging back to my car, I decided it was a north-side day, only for some reason I thought the spattering of banksias on the grass further away from the beach might be the ideal location. I drove my car with its precious cargo of bread, butter and cheese to the two-hour parking at the northern end of Bronte before meeting Morgan down on the sand, where we left our towels for the post-run swim.

We completed twenty gruelling sets along the sand before it got too hot and bright for us to comfortably sustain much more. For the final two repetitions I suggested we run with a deliberately wide gait and lean back to engage our glutes as much as possible.

Morgan and I both agreed sand running placed its own peculiar demands on the body for which shorter steps and good form were essential. While taxing in its own way, I felt that I could sustain running on the soft sand for longer than runs on hard surfaces which required a similar degree of energy. As we jogged to Tamarama I told Morgan about an article I'd read which used the word 'deep' to characterise the kind of workout sand running afforded. A couple of other runners accompanied us in our masochistic activities on the stairs, both young women, both with iPods and hats. One was walking up and down the entire set of stairs without intermission. The other was completing sprint repetitions of the top section.

As was the tradition, I frequently commented on the great fortune of the shade provided by large overhanging trees and the variation in the different sections of stairs, which offered a distraction during each repetition.

I felt fleet-footed on the first couple of sections before the lactic acid set in midway through, leaving me doubled over and heaving for breath at the top, looking out over the gully and the ocean beyond, propping up my body on the rails of the white-painted wooden fence. Morgan followed me up each time, not far behind. Five today, I suggested, as we eased our way back down the stairs with the help of the rail, passing the sprinting girl on the first flight who was completing her reps with impressive rapidity, and further down, the walking girl, who while slower was no less relentless in applying herself to the task.

At the conclusion of the final rep Morgan and I shuffled our way along, back to Bronte Beach, barely at a pace you'd call running.

A part of me was sad to leave our accomplices on the stairs and hoped that on future visits they might be there again, enjoying the shade, the steep and diverse stairs, and the dose of endorphins supplied by their bodies at the top of each flight.

We returned to our towels for a swim. As soon as I immersed my head in the water I was hit with a blur of barely graspable memories and imaginings, perhaps based on similar occasions when I'd dived into water. I often wondered whether it was my emotional consistency at the time, the temperature of the water, or other yet more obscure factors that determined which memories and imaginings were available to me during that sudden and impossible-to-predict phase change experienced when entering the wet.

After floating about for a sufficient amount of time, completing the twists and body-hugging routines I'd begun to perfect, Morgan and I headed back up the stairs to meet with his father, whom he'd instructed via text message to find us among the banksias at the north end of Bronte. We dawdled, scrupulously assessing the topography's grass cover, shade and relative flatness. There were a few groupings of people scattered evenly near the trees, roughly one group per tree. It was as though each tree functioned as a kind of house, an instrument of comfort that at once demarcated space and offered some kind of security.

I scanned the area and found an ideal spot on the edge of some shade. Another couple shared the same tree but they were on the other side, largely obscured by the trunk. Not far off a young girl, about four years old and wearing her mother's sunglasses, sat on a bench singing, while her baby brother dug extensively in the sand, admiring the dirt as it fell through his fingers. We laid out our towels and I thought I'd hold off retrieving the picnic goods from my car until Morgan's dad came to join us.

Morgan's dad wore an outfit of different blues and a broad-brim hat. He introduced himself as Graham. I could see more of Alex's face in his than Morgan's, particularly when he squinted. However, his shy and eager-to-please demeanour was at odds with that of his daughter. He said he was keen to get some insight into the development of his son, whom he described as remarkably like his great auntie, a comparison I hoped that one day I would have the chance to confirm empirically. Graham had brought along a container of figs, a salad of cabbage and lettuce heavily laden with toasted pine nuts, and some smelly cheeses. The prospect of smearing these over my fresh bread was too much to resist and I excused myself to go to the Odyssey and grab the loaf, the smell of which had permeated the car.

Back on the picnic rug we happily observed the two children still playing near the bench. The girl, having seen us, was playing to the audience, while her brother continued his mission of dirt displacement with dedication and amazement. A short way down the slope, a particularly well-groomed man was posing for what I presumed to be a promotional video for a fitness institute of some sort. I checked out his thighs and calves for signs of his ability and couldn't come to a conclusion as to whether he'd be a threat over ten kilometres.

I was glad Morgan's dad took to the loaf of bread with such gusto, since it permitted me a similar level of indiscretion with his cheese. We sat there for the most part in silence, gorging ourselves beneath the branches of the banksia bushes. I felt an immense privilege in being able to observe these two genetically related individuals at feeding time and wished Alex, her mother and perhaps her great aunt were there to complete the picture.

Nodding towards the two children at play, Graham said to Morgan, They remind me of you and Alex. The reference to her name made me feel uncomfortable and I immediately tried to steer the conversation away with a few pieces of trivia about Bronte: that it was my favourite beach due to its catering to different kinds of swimming, and that my usual practice was to picnic on the grassy slopes on either the south or the north side. Perhaps perplexed by this sudden, animated outburst, Graham added that he used to live in Randwick for a while but tended to frequent Coogee Beach most often. I asked him about willie wagtails, a topic I knew would be a reliable conversation starter with a birder, and he confirmed they were indeed in decline. He said that it was probably due to a combination of factors. The particular kind of urban environment now pervasive in Sydney tended to favour other species, he said, particularly the more aggressive noisy miners. I still see wagtails though, in places like the wild outer regions of Centennial Park, the Randwick Environment Park and the coastline stretching from Waverley Cemetery to Bondi. The trick, he said, is to find ways to include more dense, low-level shrubbery for shelter and sources of water.

I resisted sharing any stories about the bird murders I'd committed and instead told him that I would now begin to keep an eye out too. I would be grateful, I said, if you took me out sometime on one of your monitoring expeditions in the park. It's playing an increasingly central role in my life. He seemed pleased by the idea and Morgan and I agreed that it would be hard to improve on the combination of intense physical exercise in the park, a morning walk looking for birds and a picnic on the soft grass under the shade of a tree.

Morgan and Graham said goodbye after lunch, kindly leaving me the last of the figs and salad. I lay back on the grass and observed the enduringly satisfying phenomenon of unity and differentiation expressed in the branches of the trees. I reflected on the work done by my body that day and recalled the line from Morgan's diary about pretending to be crucified to the lawn. I fell asleep.

When I woke any previous hints of tiredness were eradicated, and I had an immediate feeling of liveliness and lucidity that persisted throughout the day. I decided this feeling was a gift from the trees under which I had slept.

The two children and the well-groomed man were gone but another family had set up their picnic things and a small vessel containing burning kindling. I decided this was the best spot at Bronte and ought to be my default for extended periods of horizontal relaxation. I looked at the scattered placement of banksias, stretching down the back of the hill and into the darker greens of the gully. They were outliers facing the great open stretch of the ocean, forms grown to embrace the wind. I imagined how the beach would have appeared before the intensive landscaping of white settlement and thought, perhaps fancifully, that the banksias and the undulating ground were enough to give some partial indication of what it might have been like.

Morgan's Birthday

On Morgan's birthday we again completed twenty magical soft sands down at Bronte in the first of the day's light. The plan for afterwards was to wander up the hill a bit to a café for breakfast where we would meet two of his friends.

The light that morning was an uncommonly glamorous gold, and the air still hot and thick despite the onset of autumn. The atmosphere was one of great excitement, something that would be difficult to impart just by tallying up the different elements of the scene.

We were joined in our repetitions by two others runners, who trudged through the sand, kicking up flecks and nodding as they ran past. The ocean was bustling and sharp blue. Morgan and I talked at first about what we planned to eat for breakfast. I said that I'd already made up my mind and planned to have the blood sausage. The first few reps were an unbelievable punishment: rarely had I felt such pronounced lethargy in my legs, no doubt due in part to my long double runs on the weekend and poor sleep. But after five minutes or so I was off, a completely new body having developed out of the previously reluctant thing I had been dragging around.

After ten reps I put some distance on Morgan and entered my own world. I could have been on a beach anywhere but for some reason the first candidate to lay claim to my anonymous reverie was the coastline of Cap Bon in Tunisia, which I'd familiarised myself with extensively on the internet after encountering the name on a distinctively branded tube of harissa paste, featuring a lighthouse perched on a blue ocean cliff, with a bright yellow background and a garland of red chillies like a beard at the bottom of the image.

On the coastline of Cap Bon I would tentatively make my way down through the rocks to the water's edge and look out to a horizon that placed me at what I imagined to be the very edge of the world. There was no one else in sight, the only sign of human construction the dirt road I'd taken through the hills down to the water's edge. I looked into the water at the great seething masses of seaweed, a throbbing baroque assemblage of forms shot through with occasional dusty-blue glimpses to the deeper waters below.

After twenty reps Morgan peeled off to have a quick dip before going to meet his friends up the hill at the café. When we passed each other for the last time I said I wanted to punch out a few more reps, maybe hit thirty. I'll meet you at the café, I told him. As well as feeling full of beans, I wanted to inhabit these virtual scenes of deep replenishment for as long as possible.

As I was making my way along the mid-stretch of the beach, past the surf-lifesaving club, I noticed a figure with a broom sweeping the porch that surrounded the main building. She was conversing with the lifeguards occasionally and demonstrating a good deal of concern for her duty. The figure appeared to be Coach Fitz.

The haze of the early morning light and my imaginings may have led me astray, but with each repetition past the clubhouse I became more certain. I wondered whether she'd seen me – she must have seen me. I kept a close eye on her activities, not really sure whether I wanted her to see me or not. She finished her sweeping and went down to the beach for a swim. I kept track of our probable trajectories, hoping to anticipate a chance meeting before it took me by surprise. Our paths crossed just as she was about to take the stairs back up to the concrete esplanade. Coach, I yelled, tapping her on the shoulder as I ran past. How many are you doing? she yelled out. Thirty, I said. How many have you done? Twenty-six, I said. Come and say hi afterwards, I'll be on the steps by the surf club.

I didn't have much time after my run because I was already late for Morgan's breakfast and I half wanted to sneak off up the hill, but some greater, mechanical urge pushed me to go and interrupt Coach Fitz, who was in conversation with one of the lifeguards. She broke off the conversation when she saw me and the guard hurried into the building with some flags. We talked about what we were up to and Coach said she was now working at a homeless shelter for boys, some of whom she'd regularly take to the beach for fitness sessions and swims. She said we ought to catch up and asked how things were going with my training and whether I was still living in my car. I told her of my plans to get into coaching and that I even had my first subject, who I was about to meet for breakfast up the hill. Anyway, I better go, I said, and she said, Yeah, I'll send you a message, have you still got the same number?

I went for a quick dip and had partial success convincing myself I was in the waters off the edge of Cap Bon. Either way it was a stunning morning, and I took great pleasure briefly bending and stretching my body in the water in a manner I thought might resemble mosquito larvae. Just as I was about to exit the water I threw myself back in for another bit of floating, admiring the pink and green lichen fringes dusting the tops of the rocks as I did.

Morgan was seated with his two friends at a table on the street outside the café. I didn't bother to put a shirt on because I was still sweating and sat down to my seat draped in a ratty towel and board shorts. Morgan was conversing with them in a surprisingly animated fashion, deploying references to people and phenomena of which I could only make partial sense.

He introduced me as his coach to Sam and Judy, who both expressed what seemed a slightly antagonistic, hyperbolic disbelief at our activities – *I can't believe how much you run!* – followed by mild admiration and plans of their own to initiate comparable lifestyle adjustments.

We ordered breakfast, everyone getting the same dish of blood sausage and scrambled eggs on toast, with small dishes of onion jam, yogurt and cucumber. They called him Browne, I noticed, Morgan's last name.

Morgan tilted his stool and leaned appreciatively against the outer wall of the café, staring towards the street. Judy was entering something into her phone and Sam was looking back down Bronte towards the beach. I found it hard to engage with them both and began to process the strange feelings that resulted from seeing Coach Fitz down at the beach. I was unsure whether it was these feelings that provoked my desire to turn away from my younger company, or whether the younger company provoked the turn away, back to my older mentor. I found it hard to enter into exchanges with them. Though I didn't fully appreciate it at the time, I had clearly developed great hopes my relationship with Coach Fitz and had never adequately worked through the disappointment which followed our drunken embrace in the bathroom. While the romance of my initial encounters had vanished entirely, I was resolved to maintain some kind of connection, perhaps sharing my times and progress with her online or in a diary, consulting her when exploring a peculiar landscape at pace, composing some observation about the contradictory aesthetic evinced by some building, or even inviting her on one of my training runs with Morgan.

The cooler tendrils of autumn eventually began to colonise that elongated summer and the idea of getting Morgan in peak condition for the Six Foot Track took on a new importance. I decided I would write out a training program based on extensive internet searches into running routines, my own experience and all I had learnt from Coach Fitz. The program would focus on what should be the key aim of any runner: to keep running, with the corollary that the best way to do this is to stay injury-free and to enjoy the activity. I more or less bastardised Coach's emphasis on sands and stairs at the early stages of the program. I retained many of the same formats for my sessions, incorporated a few new locations, and placed greater emphasis on continuous interval training, which I had read about on a number of blogs I favoured.

After my chance meeting with Coach Fitz at Bronte I started planning the fantasised event in a park in which I could bring the different important people from my life together. I would source my favourite produce from around the city. We would lay out a rug under a tree and everyone would congratulate me on the quality of the bread I'd discovered, at which point I would list my preferred bakeries in order. Perhaps I'd even catch Alex while she was on a trip back from London to see her family. Her dad would be there too, maybe her mum, along with my own parents who would bring a container of mixed leaf from the garden. Morgan and Coach would chat about running and I would feel comfortable enough to sit quietly, pleased that the atmosphere of intense amicability was able to continue in my absence.

When Morgan suggested that his dad might join us on a walk around Centennial Park to share his knowledge of birds, I immediately began to imagine this as a context where I could realise a partial coming together of the inspiring forces in my life. Morgan's proposition was intoxicating enough for me to suggest he meet the mentor who was in part responsible for the practices that informed my own approach to training. In no position to refuse, Morgan agreed that this was a decent enough idea and, once I had confirmed the time and place, I sent Coach a text.

Birdwatching with Morgan and His Dad in Centennial Park

I knew as soon as I saw Coach Fitz waiting with Morgan and Graham in her yellow legionnaire's cap, blue shorts and cotton shearer's singlet that today might not go as smoothly as I'd imagined. She had a set of large binoculars around her neck and when we greeted each other she pulled me into that still familiar tight embrace, which left me in a state of speechlessness for the first part of our walk.

The sense of generosity and clarity that came after our chance encounter at Bronte Beach was quickly blurred by a sickening sense of antagonism, provoked by her ridiculous outfit, her animated gawking at birds, and, most significantly, the way she seemed to make a point of regularly whispering things in Morgan's ear. I regretted not giving Morgan the background story about my relationship with Coach. I should have made things explicit so I could be assured that we would both interpret her antics with a shared sense of knowing and sympathy.

We began our walk at the kids' cycle track in the area of the park known as Fearnley Grounds. Graham had a large scope on a tripod which during pauses in our walk he would invite us to look through. Stop and listen, he said, what sounds do you hear? Coach had her hand cupped against her ear as though the air was a wall. We agreed that one sound was particularly prominent. Morgan's dad said this was the noisy miner, a native honeyeater with an aggressive disposition now dominant in many Sydney regions. What are its features? he asked. Its yellow beak. Its grey feathers. Its size: small but not too small.

Coach and I both contributed. I withdrew as soon as our enthusiasms surged together. A competitive verbal stoush was on the cards unless great discipline could be exercised.

Graham shouldered the tripod and scope and we ambled up a small incline and into a more densely vegetated area I knew vaguely from my runs. We paused to look back towards the cycleway and Graham mentioned the difference between this landscape, which consisted only of mature trees and cut grass, and the diverse vegetation types of the outer wilds we were about to enter. I like to characterise the difference as between two-dimensional and three-dimensional landscapes, he said. Coach's reticence at this point was somehow more unsettling than the contributions I had thought her likely to make. I knew these observations matched her own thoughts on landscape and habitat, and I regretted receiving Graham's teaching as confirmations of Coach's wisdom rather than fresh insights in their own right.

We followed a sand trail down to the edge of the pond at the southern perimeter of the park, stopping to observe a tiny striated pardalote and a New Holland honeyeater through the branches. Graham told us that the part of the trail which bordered the ponds was beginning to erode due to changes in rules and the behaviour of dog walkers. Previously it would only be walkers with one or two dogs, said Graham, but now you see people leading as many as seven. It might seem like a minor thing but all those extra feet put pressure on the structural integrity of the soil. When Graham spoke his voice quivered with a tension I speculated was the product of an ongoing internal argument about the contrasting needs of different beings, human and non-human. When I turned around to check on Morgan, I saw Coach was explaining some routine to him, gesturing with her hands as though unfolding something and making a fast, pitter-patter motion with her feet in the sand. I glared at Coach, who looked up and saw me, stopped her demonstration, and continued walking, as though she'd just been peddling illegal goods.

Graham pointed out an old acacia, fissured by small birds visible briefly on the outer branches before disappearing into the more obscure regions closer to the trunk. We passed through a cleared area where knee-high weeds and piles of woodchips gave the place the feel of a wasteland. Graham reanimated the area with impressively specific stories of now-vanished branches that for a while functioned as homes for birds. Coach had picked up a long, straight stick and trailed further behind with Morgan. She continued to talk and gesture, articulating what I imagined was a perverse ceremony involving self-punishment, enforced drinking rituals and fanciful speculations about architectural aesthetics. I had to confront the nasty thought that my dialogues with Morgan would be forever coloured by his knowledge there was a direct association between my interests and those of Coach Fitz. I began frantically scanning through other possible topics and disciplines I could claim as peculiar to me, but didn't get any further than bread and horseracing, neither of which seemed adequate. I even pondered appealing to shared masculine values that would exclude Coach from our conversation, but quickly realised, that even in the unlikely event that Morgan and Graham would show sympathy to such a pathetic tactic, as a woman who had no doubt been long involved in the lives of male sporting types, Coach would be well practised at disarming any attacks on this front. Perhaps I could begin a discussion about the perfect sandwich? I found the few comments Coach made on food far less convincing than her ideas about architecture and landscape. I found myself imagining opening up a restaurant that also offered personal training services. It would serve only one kind of meal, perhaps pasta, with subtle variations: with and without anchovies, fresh or tinned tomatoes, basil or parsley, an extra dollar for pine nuts, maybe a lasagne with fresh buffalo mozzarella. There would be free soda water and bread, and maybe some kind of unique, user-friendly, genuinely beneficial rewards scheme involving discounted exercise sessions or discounted meals. I'd invite Morgan, Graham, Alex and my flatmates to the opening. Not Coach.

I let these speculations carry me away from my immediate feelings of resentment. We stopped at the sheltered tables and chairs to look at some maps Graham had put together showing the distribution of small bird species in the park. My growing irritation at Coach's faux politeness and my restaurant dreams made it hard to listen actively. I started to imagine two alternative futures, one in which I would sever ties with both Coach and Morgan immediately, another where I would explain things to him truthfully, recounting the bathroom embrace in Annandale and her battles with alcoholism.

It started to rain. Ibis patrolled the grass, inserting their beaks into the soil. A man continued to push his daughter on one of the nearby swings. Graham and Coach were tapping the table, locked in an animated discussion about the feasibility of community reward schemes for citizen science initiatives and the great difficulty of communicating the value of ecosystem services. Morgan was quiet. I noticed him examining me thoughtfully on the odd occasion. He asked about our next session, something I was reluctant to disclose in the company of Coach Fitz. I said perhaps we could do Cooper Park and the eastern coastline, or head north of the bridge, through bush to Manly? I knew Coach was listening, no doubt desperate to interject with her own ideas of what we should do at this stage of the preparation.

After we said goodbye I began my walk back to the Odyssey via the Vernon Pavilion. I wanted to admire its distinctive hipped roof and remind myself of the sense of sturdiness and lightness that characterised Vernon's buildings. Corellas and galahs took to the grass in the soft rain. The corellas looked like galahs that had been living rough, as though they were having breakfast after a long night on the town.

I went inside the pavilion and sat down at a table in the darkness and began to flick through my phone to find out the date it was built and other details about its form and history. I noticed a man sitting at one of the tables. He was wearing three different shades of purple, including a pair of lavender felt brogues. He kept flicking his long fringe back from his eyes and wrote energetically in a notepad. Was it, could it be, Terry Durack?

I watched the man for a while until I was sure. I needed to consult him about my restaurant idea and to invest some of the rapidly souring surplus desire I possessed for a mentor after the morning I had spent with Coach. I yelled out: Terry! Durack! He looked up. The poor bugger. I love reading your reviews, I said. I've been reading since you started for Good Living. I enjoyed the one you wrote the other day about that place in Bondi. A nice sense of liveliness and humour. He put down his pen and motioned for me to come and sit next to him. I'm Tom, I said, I'm a keen runner who is planning to open a pasta restaurant, maybe in a small coastal town when I'm a bit older. What about Crescent Head? said Durack, I've always found it the most charming spot. I've stopped there once for a pie and custard tart on my way north to Byron Bay, sounds like a great idea! Ah, Durack, I continued, and slapped him on the back hard enough for his fringe to jolt free, I've waited a long time for this.

We sat there and talked under the shelter of the Vernon Pavilion. I secretly hoped Coach would find us there, engaged in discussions of cuisine about which she would have little of meaning to contribute. Durack showed me the piece he was currently working on, about a restaurant in the city that baked its own sourdough and served it with generous portions of house-churned butter which sat on display at a table nearby. He spoke of the current trend for service trolleys and his distaste for the compulsion to deconstruct rustic meals that had pleased people for centuries.

The rain continued, a fine gauze outside. I imagined Coach in the background while I talked to Durack, chasing ibises off the tops of bins, she was on fire, like Treebeard in *The Lord of the Rings*. She ran and paused, ran and paused, bringing her hands to her flaming head before plunging herself like an idiot into the Randwick Pond.

I looked at Durack, teeth so white, outfit so distinctive, fringe so lustrous and floppy, speech so elaborate and dynamic. A small bird, a willie wagtail, came and sat on the sandstone ledge of the pavilion and began to sing its pretty song, swivelling and flicking its tail as though it had some message for us to decode.

Coming Clean with Morgan

I arranged to meet Morgan at Cooper Park at 5 p.m. We would complete a series of circuits through the park and then I'd planned to deaden the nerves with a couple of excellent beers from Platinum Liquor on Bellevue Road which we would drink together overlooking the park as the sun set. I would tell him about Coach Fitz and about my relationship with Alex. I would give him the facts as best I could so he was empowered to make a judgement on the situation.

We started at the stairs and took the route down, across the grassy field into the cool damp of the lower park. My first run through the park with Coach Fitz was on my mind, the memory of her yellow cap, now a tattered flag, flapping in the breeze.

The cumulative fatigue of my recent training load made it impossible to enact my dreams of gliding and springing. I could hear Morgan skidding behind me and with my mind on other things and my body not as responsive as it was usually I went too hard into a bend and lost my footing on the loose gravel. I landed softly and tumbled over and over into a creeper of some kind that grew on the upper bank of the gully.

The blur of the fall faded into the background as I looked up at Morgan, clear and distinct standing over me, hands on his hips. As though my words were dislodged by the accident, or perhaps encouraged by this position of abasement, I began my confession: I have something to tell you, I said. I had a strange altercation with Coach Fitz before you and I met and we had stopped seeing each other due to awkwardness. She hugged me naked in the bathroom at her house after drinking the better part of a bottle of gin and then I left, rapidly. I have all kinds of unsubstantiated and problematic theories about her history that are often reflexively employed when trying to understand the choices and fortunes of single women of a certain age. As a small gesture of camaraderie, I resolved to do my best to think of her simply as an enigma. But now I can't stand the thought of her. I bumped into her on the morning of your birthday, after severing contact, and felt a strong urge to orchestrate a meeting. I had hoped we might even join in a few training sessions together.

Morgan held out an arm which I grabbed, and he leaned back as I pulled myself up. And I also need to tell you about Alex and me, I said, dusting the dirt and leaves from my front. We parted on bad terms, at least from my perspective. When she got in contact again an old ember of hope began to glow, ridiculously, and I started to fantasise about how my achievements as a runner and attitude as a coach might be transmitted back to her, and revive the ideal image I believed she must have formed of me at some point during our travels. Morgan smiled, our arms still linked. Pretty creepy behaviour from you, he said. Pretty creepy.

As we walked down the path into the dim of the rainforest, my initial ambivalence to Morgan's tone resolved into a feeling more wholeheartedly positive. I understood the flippancy I'd registered was in fact exactly the kind of presumptuous play I'd hoped would come to characterise our relations. Convinced of this, I began to talk animatedly about how irritated I was about Coach's lack of self-awareness, about her rudeness to waiters, her conceit and warped expectations. Something changed in Morgan too. He began to use his arms more while talking and chimed in with an anecdote about a friend's father who was also often rude in restaurants.

The emotional discussion exhausted my desire to run and it seemed natural to walk along and continue to talk in this peaceful way as we crossed to the northern side of the creek and took the stairs up to some higher ground above the gully.

The bush was established enough to make the city feel as though it were a dream. I referred Morgan to the canopy of trees and the different strata of vegetation beneath, pointing out how light filtered according to the distinctive vegetative, geological and atmospheric features, and asked whether he too felt as though the musty yet paradoxically refreshing air might have been doing our lungs the world of good? Morgan gave the impression he was considering the idea without offering a verbal response.

New stones had been laid in the path, with a shiny rail that contrasted with the original dry sandstone masonry. Our conversation shifted to things other than Coach. To our plan for the final month before the Six Foot Track and how long we should taper. To whether or not we should stop doing demanding hills, whether we needed one or two more gruelling long runs. How much speed work to do each week. Whether there were any glaring omissions from our program.

We emerged from the dim blanket of the lower park and the sky once again impressed itself upon us. A woman had set herself up with an easel on one of the platforms that jutted out from the track into the bush. We said hello and watched over her shoulder for a while as our shared view was redirected through her mind and then onto the canvas. The skyscrapers of Bondi Junction, the bats circling in the indigo and light orange, the vegetated slopes darkening from bright green to black.

When we reached Bellevue Road I began to feel guilty for not having completed a session and said that we both ought to make up for it independently tomorrow. Despite Coach's troubles with the bottle never being far from my mind, more than anything I was keen to show Morgan the selection of beers in Platinum Liquor nearby on Bellevue Road, and hopefully even snare an Orval that we would enjoy on a bench together overlooking the park. I justified my desire with the rationale that it was better to inoculate oneself against the extremes of addictive behaviour through small, carefully chosen pleasures, rather than complete avoidance.

Platinum Liquor had one of the best selections of beers in Sydney. Entire walls were taken up with the display of contrasting bottles and labels, little capsules detailing origin stories and aesthetic intent. Despite this abundant variety, Orval was the only beer I was hoping they had in stock. It had been brewed since 1931 by a group of Belgian monks. The bottle was made of dark glass, had a blue label and a bulging, pear-shaped bottom. I'd tried it on one previous occasion, after reading it was the best beer to have when hungover. I remembered its biscuity, savoury effervescence and the feeling of lightness it induced. Hearing it referred to as 'liquid bread' and the imagery of the monastery revealed on internet searches cemented its place alongside the *Best Bets* and Good Living as one of those exemplary things I needed to have.

We scanned the walls. I couldn't see any Orval. I asked the proprietor, an older man in a short-sleeved shirt. It was his son's shop, he knew of the beer but didn't think there was any in stock. He gave me the landline phone and said to call his son.

I spoke to his son for a while who told me it was increasingly hard to source but that he might have some in the garage and he would tell his dad to go out and check. I waited expectantly, exchanging nervous glances with Morgan who I hoped would inherit my fascination with this particular beer and use the information to obtain a sense of superiority over his friends.

When the man came back in clutching a few dusty bottles of Orval I couldn't resist slapping Morgan on the back. I bought four, giddy with excitement and already mapping out the future occasions where I would drink the remaining bottles.

Morgan and I sat for a while sharing sips from a bottle on one of the benches overlooking the park. I thought about framing our indulgence with a short discourse on austerity or begin practising some knowledge dissemination about food and drink, but I found the idea of being an authority of any kind too exhausting and didn't want to risk ruining the beer.

Morgan said that he'd noticed his body adapting to the increased training volume. I reminded him that we needed to ensure our bodies were free of any cumulative fatigue before the race and we decided to limit our hills sessions to one or two two-track sessions, one quality longish run on a Sunday at marathon pace, and then two easy longer runs. And that should do it.

I enjoyed the soft abundance of the bubbles in the beer, and the sense of it being at once creamy and savoury. I think I prefer a view over trees to a view over water, I said, as we looked out over the park, as though experiencing these two alternatives as a choice to evaluate for perhaps the first time in my life. I think I'm the same, he said.

The Last Hit-out

I was struck with the worst flu I'd had in at least five years in the lead-up to the race. My housemates were impossibly nice, with Chloe insisting I drink her special brew of immunity-boosting tea, which contained ginger, garlic, lemon, cayenne pepper and a tiny bit of honey.

I tried to persist with window-washing on the first day the sickness set in, one of the most challenging, unpleasant experiences of my time in the job. Rushing through the CBD with my bucket, squeegee and swab, blue rags tucked into my oversized shorts, my baggy thick grey cotton shirt was already soaked in sweat after the first shopfront. Everything was several times more exhausting than usual. I could only bring myself to eat fruit and vegetables throughout the day, though I had weird cravings for pickles and potato. I worked away in a haze of pain, mumbling to myself about how difficult things were. When everyone saw my state that evening, drooling and shaking on my bed, they convinced me it would be ridiculous to try and work the next day, so I called in for my first ever sick day.

To make matters worse, the illness coincided with a period of extreme wet and humidity. The healthy self I once knew, who experienced the delights of sunshine, exercise, expansive movement and a diverse, insatiable appetite seemed now another being entirely, as though completely inaccessible. The rain was torrential at times. The house seemed to swell and an extra layer of dirt and moisture covered its surfaces. On the rare occasion I did venture outside little activities like going to the shops to buy food seemed an achievement of great magnitude. I suspected my illness was as explicit to everyone as it was to me and assumed they were wondering what had gone wrong.

The only thing that took my mind off this extreme discomfort was following Morgan's activities on Strava. From my mucus-filled cocoon I would check continually to see if he'd been out for a run, whether he had set any personal records for the various segments into which the city had been carved by this app: Three Ponds Push, Randwick Gates to Musgrave Avenue, The Pass, The Hockeystick, uphill dodging dogs, Macca's Hill, and so on. Sometimes Morgan would give a cryptic description to his run on Strava that was vaguely reminiscent of the prose in his diary: 'The weather was supposed to be a bit hotter but the combination of the wind and the wet ground from last night's rain made for good going. I felt like an aggravated ball. Awful limping weak-souled run north, with a small intrusion into bush and back along the soft sand in shoes before a swim…'

I could also see how many kilometres he was doing each week, how fast he was running each kilometre segment and the total elevation gained. My general reading of his performance was positive. He seemed to be adapting remarkably well to the increase in training volume and quality. It was particularly encouraging to see how strong he was in the latter part of his tempo sessions (sessions of thirty to forty minutes at a pace that was comfortable yet hard).

I began to wonder whether I'd prefer Morgan or myself to do well in the run. I remembered having the same thoughts before a father-and-son running carnival during primary school. I was pitted against the other boys in my year, as my dad was against the fathers of my friends. I desperately wanted him to beat the father of my best friend, the boy with whom I was most competitive. I was going through a religious phase, largely due to my fear of the dark, and after some deliberation decided that if I was forced to make a choice I would prefer my dad to win rather than me and said a prayer to God wishing as much. I was on a training run when I made this decision and I remember something which now seems as though it must have been an artefact of my imagination: the clouds parted and a beam of light shot through, as though shining a spotlight on the virtuous decision I had just made.

On my first sessions after my bout of illness it felt like I was running in a different body. I kept picturing Bambi trying to stand up on an ice-covered lake. Where was the rhythm, the balance? Those subtle though essential binding forces that made separate energies cohere.

I arranged to meet Morgan at Trumper Park. I figured it had been nearly three months since my last visit and I wanted to pay my respects to the place before the big race. I caught the train from Redfern to Edgecliff and took the path down from New McLean Street, through the fringe of the bush. The clouds had almost entirely cleared from the sky and the morning was stunning enough to be the most regular point of remark for the women and one man in the exercise group that I joined under the shade of the Trumper Stand while waiting for Morgan. They all seemed to have South African accents and performed star jumps, burpees and short runs around the perimeter of the oval. The leader had a dog, a caramel Staffordshire terrier, who nested in a rug with a blue ball that it chewed on with great affection. They too valued the oval, regularly remarking on how green and lush it was, its surface illuminated by the morning sun, while the bush behind, leading back to the station, remained a shady mass gradually emerging into higher resolution. I wondered if they knew about the track through the bush that led up behind the park, whether they admired the large Moreton Bay figs and the duck pond at the old quarry site. A lone magpie stood near the pitch in the middle of the oval and a couple of other people were reading books on the seats in the stand nearby.

I put on my earphones and pressed shuffle. 'Dreams' by The Cranberries started playing. I had downloaded the track in a fit of euphoria after a chance encounter on the radio. The morning sunshine, the setting and the music were an intense contrast with the recent period of rain and illness. I found myself dazed by happiness and unable to follow a thought. Now it was my ill self and the dim weather that seemed impossible. I had an abstract, rational sense the weather had changed and I'd been sick. Yet at a more basic, barely conscious level, there was an unbridgeable gap between the two different perspectives. My current self was completely other.

In the midst of this I spotted Morgan running along the outside of the track, drink bottle hugged under his arm and hat pulled down over his eyes. He was running with a newfound flow and stability: looking relaxed, moving quick. Due to some unaccountable compulsion I found myself looking to the sky. In rushed the sour convulsions and the blissful inward turn of perception that came with tears: I was pure feeling, my hopes directed towards this running partner who carried an entire world inside him. By the time Morgan arrived my cheeks were wet. I hurried down onto the field and in a bid to distract him and began speaking in detail about the session and striding crabwise out towards the middle of the field.

The session was six by one kilometres, each kilometre about two-and-a-half laps of the oval. Despite the surface looking impeccable from a distance, closer inspection revealed some variation, with lumpy patches and less cover in some areas. A young family was playing in the cricket nets on the edge of the field, so we had to adjust our loops to accommodate them.

I started out strong, settling about five metres in front of Morgan. I felt a regained sense of rhythm. It was invigorating to once again feel the density and texture of the ground and a sense of my body accumulating distance as it moved. I held my lead for the first kilometre and rested immediately with my hands on my knees. Morgan wandered around, breathing deeply, hands on his head. We ran on every five minutes. With the first lap taking three minutes and forty seconds, we got about one minute twenty rest. I started strongly again, but I could hear Morgan closer behind. With more effort I managed to keep a similar pace and still finished narrowly in front. We followed the same pattern for the next repetitions, though each became harder and the rest time seemed to finish as soon as it began.

Things changed for the last two reps. I shot out at the start each time, but at about the 300-metre mark Morgan reeled me in and continued to increase his lead by increments until we finished the kilometre. He rested in the same way, standing tall and wandering in spirals. I wanted to lie on the ground after the fifth rep but managed to stay upright, albeit bent over and puffing heavily. You're going strong, I managed to gasp.

Morgan took the lead from the beginning of the final rep. I attempted to stay on his heels and just enjoy the run, the dew on the edges of my feet, the tilt and thrust of my body rounding the bend, the open encouragement of the straights. I watched Morgan's back, watched him stride out as though a small engine was situated just behind his body, pushing him forward with a hidden extra charge. It seemed less like he was fighting the air with his style, more like something splashing and collecting itself at the same time.

We lay on the grass together, bodies propped on our hands in the grass and heads tilted up to the sky. The calls from the boot-camp group could still be heard over towards the small grandstand: Keep it going, Jenny, now knee-raises. You're going well, I said to Morgan again, what are you eating? Mainly oats, he said, and lots of cheese in the evenings. No different really. Chocolate. You're doing something right, you ran through those nicely. Are you feeling better? he asked. Much, I said. Still a bit dusty towards the end but I've got my body back. Ugh, being sick is a nuisance.

I walked with Morgan back up to Edgecliff Station and said goodbye: I might see you again before the race but otherwise I'll be in touch. Say hi to Graham, I said, hoping to sense whether Morgan had also resisted sharing the coincidence with his father as well.

I bought a grapefruit from Harris Farm and walked up Edgecliff Road to where I had sometimes parked the Odyssey to sleep. As I walked I thought about the memories distributed across this area and the sense that if I paid attention to them I possessed a kind of map, which animated the place and gave me a kind of special access. I thought about the apartment where my friend once lived and where I purposely burnt myself on a pair of metal scissors that I had heated in the oven, to bring myself out of a patch of tiredness that was making going to the pub a less appealing prospect; about the birthday party in one of the larger houses where I worked as a waiter, the birthday girl and her family encouraging me to work with my shirt off for an extra fifty dollars. I thought about the cricket nets in Cooper Park that were just down the hill behind the houses on the left side of the road, about the various now forgotten houses where I had washed windows: a temporary trespasser speculating about the lives of the inhabitants based on glimpses of family photographs and other fragments of life seen while cleaning the inside glass.

By the time I got to where I used to park the Odyssey I had peeled and eaten my grapefruit. I remembered the smells that permeated the car and the deposits of paraphernalia which gave some vague indication of my routines and preferences: little collections of tissue paper, paperclips, coins, apple cores, stray almonds, bottle caps and dried citrus peel in its various pouches and holders. I felt an enduring sense of satisfaction at Morgan's progress. It was pleasing to know the competitive spirit didn't only hinge on beating an opponent. I shared in his potential in a way that was similar to the warm feeling I got thinking about certain racehorses I admired. The mere thought of it, the turning over of his capacity in my mind, seemed to fill the future with a sense of possibility, and blotted out the importance I had previously placed on his association with Alex.

I wandered back down Edgecliff Road thinking about what I might cook my flatmates for dinner: perhaps something with eggplant, maybe a curry? I could make fresh naan bread. What about pasta? Or Mexican beans? I could still make a naan bread and have it with beans? But pasta is very good. This line of thinking seemed to occupy me for the entire trip back until the desire for pasta grew to occupy such a large space in my mind that I found myself in the kitchen making the sauce.

The Day Before

I picked up my bib from the Carrington Hotel in Katoomba on the Friday before the race. The Carrington was a majestic nineteenth-century hotel overlooking the rest of the town. There was an atmosphere of excitement at the venue, with runners milling about the veranda enjoying beers and chatting about past events and race strategy. This little pre-race-day ritual made the run a reality in a way I hadn't anticipated. I looked through the race list and found the number associated with my bib and name: 396. I checked to make sure Morgan was on the list and then, after hesitating for a while, checked the last name Fitzgerald. Her name wasn't there: Fenton, then Fynch. The man behind the desk said, Make sure you check both columns, and then I saw that the column of names on the right-hand side of the page proceeded alternately in pace with the left – something that for some reason I wanted to tell the man was counter to what people would expect and should be remedied next year. Fenton in the left-hand column, then, on the right, Fitzgerald. I felt an immediate sense of apprehension, which quickly transformed to a feeling of conviction tinged by apprehension. Coach Fitz would be joining us on the starting line. I speculated about her condition, what kind of training she would have been doing, whether she'd focused enough on hills and off-road running, or if she had managed to include more fast downhill-track sessions, which I'd started to believe was the glaring absence in my program with Morgan. Should I ignore her, or act in a sporting fashion and wish her well? Should I make it a race about Coach Fitz, or treat her as just one other runner in a race more about myself, Morgan and the particular challenges of the track?

I checked into my strange little motel on the highway, thinking of American films involving criminals, guns, listening through thin walls and hiding important items in places around the room. I sat on the edge of my bed and looked at my feet and the bad carpet they were resting on. The word *pedestal* echoed through my head: these poor little buggers on which my entire posture depended, even an injured toe would be enough to entirely transform my gait. My little toes were peculiar-looking things. The toenail was more like a retarded claw. My dad had exactly the same deformity.

It looked like a little cartoon composed from rudimentary lines and facial features: Hello little fellow, you and I will take on the Coach. What's that? Yes, I agree, she is an embarrassment and she will hopefully succumb to the pre-race-day excitement at the Carrington and destroy herself with drink.

Morgan and Graham were in an Airbnb in Katoomba. We met for dinner at a place called The Garage and shared a huge platter of figs, cheeses, smoked trout, roast vegetables, seasoned chickpeas, some kind of avocado-based dip and crackers. I also got a serving of chips and aioli. I mentioned several times over the course of the evening that some crusty bread would have been the only improvement possible on an otherwise perfect meal and pointed out the awful clock tower that extended from a blond-brick building on the other side of the road. It is an abomination, I said, enjoying the measure of hyperbole in the word. Graham was looking forward to getting in some birdwatching after he watched the start of the race, and said they'd already seen a lyrebird not far from their house. He would then drive to Jenolan Caves to meet us, and had kindly offered to give me a lift back to Sydney. Sadly Morgan's mum, Cynthia, was away for work, as often seemed to be the case.

Morgan seemed focused, perhaps a little nervous, and very hungry. I resisted the urge to share my news about Coach Fitz and instead observed father and son devouring their meals. It was an enthralling spectacle. I imagined the unseen metabolic processes by which the food Morgan ate would be converted into energy that would be expended during the run, and the other processes, dissipated in time yet still persisting, that allowed Graham and

Cynthia to produce Morgan and Alex. I was overcome by a deep need to cook for them all, to source ingredients which I would subject to the influences of heat and various techniques of pulverisation, before serving a great meal to the family, and as they ate I would sit and watch contentedly, at once part of the spectacle and yet distinct, watching the food I had prepared become incorporated into their metabolic processes and perhaps even their dreams, as they lay in bed at night, shreds of consciousness still flickering in their otherwise dormant bodies.

Would you like some of my dip? asked Morgan. The two of them looked at me while they chewed. No, no, I'm fine, I said, scraping the last of the aioli with a chip and turning to look up at the clock tower.

Sleep like a log, said Graham, as we parted. Yeah, sleep well, said Morgan. You too, I said, and walked with a rare sense of purpose into the rapidly cooling, unmistakeably autumnal evening.

I prepared my race-day kit back at the motel, exorcising my anxiety through folding and placing my clothes in different locations, pinning my bib to my singlet and laying out breakfast things for a quick meal and tea before the run. I decided on a light meal of rolled oats with milk and sultanas and a cup of black tea. I prepared my race-day playlist and checked the various apparatuses, such as the waterproof sleeve for my phone and my tiny backpack in which I placed several sesame bars and some cash for coffee after the race.

I'd picked up a book about the 1970s from a stack on the side of the road, and lay in bed reading about the fraught making of

Apocalypse Now. I couldn't help composing an alternate narrative that ran alongside my reading which featured Coach Fitz as a combination of Colonel Kurtz in the film and the overweight and cantankerous Marlon Brando. I imagined Coach appearing on race day with a freshly shaven head, globs of sunscreen around her ears, her bird-like body darting swiftly through the bush like one of the bush turkeys that were beginning to appear more frequently in the parks around Sydney. We faced each other partially submerged, in the brown, sandy water of a river, Coach's eyes just above the surface.

I was disappointed to wake in the night after another subconscious ejaculation. I traced back through the contents of my dream, perplexed such imagery could stir this kind of physiological response. I had been teaching Morgan how to shoot a bow and arrow. The arrows were transparent, made of perspex or glass and filled with water. We grappled with the weapon together. He guided me through the appropriate poses, wrapping my body in his as we looked down the arrow together, out over the gentle swell of some anonymous beach. Satisfied that I had now learnt the art, Morgan began to walk away, and as he did he transformed into a somewhat feminine boy from my high school who matured rapidly in the later years while still retaining some of his feminine traits like smooth skin, large eyelashes and a high-pitched voice. I aimed the arrow at his body and shot, the arrow lifted on its trajectory and struck him in the back of the head, breaking in two and leaking its fluid out onto the ground. The front half of the arrow was fixed in the back of his skull. He reached up to it with his hand and turned to face me in disbelief. The dream then transformed unaccountably into another sequence of events related to the first only by the beachfront setting, involving the dislodging of a great whale wedged into a gap between some rocks deep beneath the ocean.

Race Day

I woke at 5.50 a.m., had my breakfast and began the short jog along the highway to the start line at the Explorers Tree. It was still dark at the beginning of the jog but by the time I got to the tree the first of the daylight revealed runners emerging from houses and cars around the area. A great variety of styles of sportswear, body type and equipment was on view: some runners with multiple tubes spraying out from the sides of their backpacks and drink bottles tucked into any spare patch of cloth, while others wore nothing but a light singlet and cap.

A dirt trail led from the highway through the bush to the marshalling area, where a crowd gathered beneath a large banner. A man on a microphone talked continuously and music played in the background. I looked for Morgan and Graham but couldn't find them so I pushed my way through the crowd towards the starting line, ready to start the race solo if necessary. The gathering of bodies in the bush bounced and stretched, at once unified and multiple, producing a palpable elevation in temperature and a vaguely detectable moistness. The surrounding movements induced a sense of shared agitation and I couldn't help but look for Morgan in a frenetic, distracted fashion. I closed my eyes and attempted to compose myself in the crowd. The man on the microphone said we were inside a minute. I felt a hand on my shoulder and turned. It was Coach. She waved in my face, Good luck in the run, Tom, the Six Foot Track! I nodded and said good luck, turning again to the front, my nerves edging from a pleasant sense of anticipation towards nausea. I felt another tap on my shoulder and turned to find Morgan, face glistening with sunscreen and sebum, hair tucked behind his ears and eyes partially shaded by a blue baseball cap. I smiled and pointed to Coach, who looked at Morgan and waved. Morgan looked at me, then I saw him lean across a couple of bodies in-between, grab the front of Coach's shirt and say, with a smile which conveyed a great certainty, I'm young and I'll eat you alive, then a pause, take it with grace. And Morgan returned to his upright position in the crowd, leaving Coach to compute the significance, not so much of the meaning of this interjection, but of what might have driven Morgan to make it. Or at least this is how I imagined things in the peculiarly fleeting and yet elongated period that at once seemed to dissipate and extend in the final countdown. Ten, nine, eight, seven, six, five, four, three, two, one and we're off.

The first part of the run was particularly hairy, a steep, muddy downhill, some parts with stairs, others with loose vines. The track was only wide enough to run in single file, with a small space for overtaking if the front runner moved to the side. There was plenty of chat about people running slower than each other's grandmothers, and sometimes compelling, sometimes desperate expressions of camaraderie. I quickly lost any sense of where Morgan or Coach were.

The slick, narrow trail opened up onto a wider, sandy track where I felt more comfortable. I picked up the pace and found myself sailing past a few runners. I wondered at this point whether I was pushing it too hard, thinking I was running at about half-marathon pace. I wanted to capitalise on the speed afforded by this type of terrain, and yet I was aware it was all about keeping it together on the 'back nine'. I kept up the pace, buoyed on by the feeling of passing other runners with relative ease.

The terrain opened up even further and I went from being a runner who was part of a pack to a runner alone, facing the persistent internal analysis of my mind: was my state now a good indication of how I would feel later? Were the two unrelated? How do I feel now compared to other runs I have been on? Would I continue to feel more limber? Or was this the peak, the best it was going to get?

I was now running through what were more or less paddocks. I could see the runners in front of me spaced out on the coming hills and valleys, almost as though they occupied an alternate reality, a picture on the page of a book. There were always footsteps and breathing behind me but I never looked around. We went up and down hills and valleys, across small streams, the track bent tightly around rocks and roots, smells emerging of smoke and the refreshing cinnamon-citrus of eucalypts as they began to dry out in the day.

By the time we got to the Coxs River the seeds of doubt that I'd been able to repress earlier in the run were now starting to flourish. I waded across the river, annoyed by its wetness and by my sloppy, heavy shoes for the run up the steep mongrel of a fire trail to come.

Every three kilometres there was a drink station with surprisingly enthusiastic and encouraging firefighters pointing out the different kinds of refreshment and nutrition on the fold-out tables before them: water on this side, sports drink on the other, banana, watermelon and lolly snakes. You're going well, mate! I looked up at the climb before me, legs oddly immobile, as though some toxin had begun to crystallise in the muscle and I was now, as I began the ascent, starting to turn to stone.

Runners went past, one, two, three, four, moving slowly but with comparative ease. At first the sight of the constantly growing gap they opened up in front of me added to my suffering, but before long it didn't bother me and I came to the decision I must run my own race. The course itself was my competitor.

The sky became more prominent as I trudged onwards: the clearest and most striking blue, about as dark as a blue sky got, but bright. The trees thinned, the ground became lighter and eventually I reached what appeared to be the ridgeline. I heard steps and breathing and put my head down to ignore yet more salt in my wounds. Give us a smile, cobber! It was Coach, her stride still long, legs moving smoothly. The punishment of the run had lulled me into a volatile combination of obsequiousness and frustration. I yelled good luck, concerned more by my own plight and the twenty-odd kilometres I still had to run than by Coach's seeming success. I watched her gradually gap me until before long she disappeared altogether.

For a while my only company was at the drink stations. Some of the firefighters had gotten bored enough to compose elaborate spruiking routines aimed to inform and entice runners into drinking the various beverages and food. I heard them cheer 'A banana!' as I picked half a banana and ran past. My stops at the stations became longer and my ability to expend energy decoding the sentiment in their manner decreased. Rather than distinguish between the different drinks I simply drank one of each, which by this stage included cola and green tea in addition to water and sports drink.

I decided it was time for music, my last resort. I had composed a playlist mainly featuring Carly Rae Jepsen and a group called Chvrches. I hoped the music, as it had done on occasions before, would replace the sensory atmosphere of debilitating soreness and fatigue with something lighter and more uplifting. To begin with it had a mild influence. I focused my energies inward and the frenetic cycles of doubt-filled analysis dissolved into a hazy narrative given coherence by the mood of each song. I was now running through a forest of native cypress. A man with impossibly thin calves jogged past, then another who looked almost fifty, then a woman in a bright two-piece lycra running outfit and visor. Insulated in the weak fantasy afforded by my music, I watched them edge ahead ,then disappear.

Soon the effect of the music wore off and its bubbly vitality became incongruous and irritating, grating on my need to suffer in peace. I put the earphones back in my pocket and drudged on, maybe only ten kilometres to go. Runners passed more frequently now. One brushed past quite close and held out a hand as they did for a high five. It was Morgan. I responded with a reflex slap and said, Go Morgan, catch Coach! I caught a look of determined joyousness in his eyes. Almost the polar opposite of the grimace I imagined expressed my own sense of vulnerability and despair. I watched Morgan's stride:

how was it that his body was able to sustain the jolts of the steepening downhill and the loose stones as though the run was just beginning? How was it possible for him to move with such lightness and speed after more than thirty kilometres?

I drew on my ability to imagine and commit to a new self-conception. I was now the ageing warrior. Doing the rounds just for the hell of it, to be out there in the bush, suffering through the task we had set ourselves with no aspirations or need for a measure of success. I was visited by darker thoughts too, about how my lack of zest in the race was due to a deeper, internal awareness that the adventure I had started with Morgan was a fraud, and that at some point, the story would become a legend told within the family where I played the role of pervert and fool.

On the final descent the track thinned to a scree-ridden trail cut into the side of the mountain. I cursed every loose rock and imagined an agent conspiring against me whenever I stumbled. The pain was enough to provoke uninhibited groans and cursing. My only respite was the thought that with every step the end edged closer and I was now within five kilometres of it. I was continually passed by other runners whom I accommodated by edging over to the side of the trail in an exaggeratedly hospitable fashion. I was at the stage of the fight where I wanted to be put out of my misery.

The view out over the treetops was spectacular. Large boulders and raw cliff faces cut into the hazy blue-grey-green foliage. Birds sang and mixed with the rattle of cowbells and the distant, continuous cheer at the finish line. Yet I felt none of the uplift familiar to me from looking into the distance from the top of Tamarama steps, or on any of my other spectacular training runs. I wondered whether this was what it would be like to die in a beautiful landscape: an environment of unsurpassed splendour, utterly indifferent to the great pathos of human experience.

By the time I began the stretch along the cement path to Caves House and the race's finish, my range of movement had narrowed to little more than a shuffle. I dragged myself along, caught in a web of my own pain. My thoughts were skittish and incoherent. I felt a great craving that lacked an object. More runners went past and even on the final stretch of the race, where I might usually muster a challenge no matter how wretched my state, I merely slowed to let a runner pass, to get it over with and make explicit that there would be no resistance from this ruined competitor.

I saw Morgan and Graham at the line, ran through to receive my obligatory medal and gift bag in a daze, then relied on Morgan and Graham to usher me to a secluded spot near one of the cool rooms at the barbecue area. I haphazardly spread my paraphernalia about on the wood chips and dirt and put my distorted form to rest under a veil of autonomous blackness. I lay there not quite asleep, mumbling to my company to reassure them of my consciousness.

Slowly, with no more new pain to undergo, the post-race endorphins began to do their work and a gradually building sense of elation began. This feeling continued, helped by the supplementary influence of caffeine, for the entire three-hour car trip back to Sydney with Morgan and Graham, and well into the evening, where the few drinks shared with my housemates in the backyard had such a profound effect on my renewed metabolism that I felt as though

I was a young boy again, intoxicating myself with great ease at the teat of a warm Tooheys Red in a paddock by the light of the moon.

Of course we talked often of the moment Morgan overtook Coach, within a kilometre of the finish line. The final downhill got the better of her, as it did for many runners. Her quads were gone. I liked to imagine she tried to trip Morgan or reached out to grab his shirt as he ran past and Morgan slapped her hand away and ran on strongly. Coach, you pathetic fool. But no, in reality the run invites acquiescence, not trickery, and Coach would have seen many a Morgan run past in her time.

*W*here water meets land and day
meets night they swim with their dogs. Little pools of ocean in rock,
orphaned jewels from anonymous mass. Fringes of pellucid green brush
against bodies as they explore the underwater world. Maps of moss and
lichen in yellow, pink and purple. Beards of open barnacles and stray
crabs on latitudinal shuffles into and out of apertures of rock.

They play at this level platform, this midpoint, terrain and marine.
They survey and swim. They plunge their bodies. The repetition of a
profane baptism where the swelling water is pierced by and carries the
fleshy, breathing bodies.

They come to participate in its abundance. The loose mould that
lubricates our minds with ill-formed memories of the warm matrix
where we were carried. We are carried again.

I prepare my picnic, my rustic delights. I tear the nub from my loaf
and inspect the catacombs inside, air fossils in a fluffy white explosion
obscured by caramel crust. I dip the bread in oil, its newly broken
surfaces mapped by a slick layer of mineral green. Immersed in my

eating I survey the bodies of this outcrop. All gymnasts, all practitioners of bathing, of floating, of atmospheric transformation.

I watch the surface waiting for it to be disturbed by a particular body. A body will come from the water and walk towards me.

The nucleus of this novel was formed during a period of travel in 2014 made possible by the Marten Bequest Scholarship.

The Giramondo Publishing Company acknowledges the support of Western Sydney University in the implementation of its book publishing program.

This project has been assisted by the Commonwealth Government through the Australia Council, its arts funding and advisory body.